# No Time On Our Side

#1974305

# No Time On Our Side

**Roger Chapman**

Drawings by Peter A. G. Milne

ANDERSONIAN LIBRARY
BAIRD HALL
COLLECTION
UNIVERSITY OF STRATHCLYDE

 **Nautical**

Copyright © 1975 by Roger R. Chapman

Maps and Drawings
Copyright © 1975 by Nautical Publishing Company Limited

First published June 1975 by

NAUTICAL PUBLISHING COMPANY LIMITED
Nautical House, Lymington, Hampshire, England

in association with
George G. Harrap and Company Limited, London

ISBN 0 245 525734

UNIVERSITY OF STRATHCLYDE
26 JUL 1989
UNIVERSITY LIBRARY

Filmset and printed in Great Britain by
BAS Printers Limited, Wallop, Hampshire

D
623.8887
CHA

This book is dedicated to Peter Messervy, Bob Eastaugh and their magnificent rescue team from many parts of the world who battled without sleep for $3\frac{1}{2}$ days to bring Roger Mallinson and myself to safety from the darkness of the Atlantic deep—back to our wives and families.

# Acknowledgements

I would like to take this opportunity to thank the people who, during and after the rescue of *Pisces III*, provided help, understanding and assistance in writing this book.

First to my wife June, who behaved so calmly during the dark hours of the rescue, having complete faith in the heroes of this story, the rescuers who were struggling out at sea. Also George Henson and his wife Marjorie, who provided the quiet family background where she stayed and where we both returned immediately after my return to Barrow.

In compiling this book I would like to thank Commander and Mrs Erroll Bruce for their personal assistance and hospitality in their home. At Nautical Publishing, all the staff and especially Janet Dent for typing many amended copies of the manuscript.

To Peter Milne for the sketches. And particularly to Vickers Limited, and Vickers Oceanics Limited for extensive use of reports, material and the many photographs; also Captain R. B. Moss of the USNR in Washington for pictures of *CURV*. Also to the *Daily Express* for the photos on pages 84, 104, 123, 146, 147 (upper), 150 and 152.

# Contents

# Foreword

By the Rt. Hon. Lord Robens of Woldingham,

P.C., D.C.L., L.L.D.

In this fast moving world where instant communication makes every noteworthy event anywhere in the world known everywhere else in the world in almost the twinkling of an eye, yesterday's news becomes almost as old as the penny farthing bicycle, and there are few happenings that hold the world stage over twenty-four hours. In my recollection there have been just two in these last few years, when the whole world was agog to know almost hourly what was to happen next.

The first was the return of the astronauts from the moon in a damaged space capsule, and the second when Roger Chapman and Roger Mallinson, entombed in *Pisces III*, a steel spherical submersible, lay for just over three days 1,575 feet below the surface of the Atlantic Ocean.

In both cases, human beings had to rely on outside help for successful rescue and their own indomitable courage and nerve for survival.

In both cases, when the rescue operation was successfully concluded, the world breathed a sigh of relief and the more devout a silent prayer, and life went on as usual.

Many people, however, must have wanted to know what it really must have felt like to be waiting, in the case of the two Rogers, in the cold darkness in such cramped conditions that little movement was possible. How could they possibly deal with normal human requirements? What passed through their minds? What did they talk about as the hours went by, and how as the precious hours went by were they able to keep their nerve?

We shall always be grateful to Roger Chapman for setting

down in simple language the whole story and the answers to these questions and many others in this book.

As Chairman of Vickers, I was proud of heading up an organisation which has probably more submarine experience than any other company in the world, and which could produce such a team of competence and quality on the surface, for Roger Chapman never to lose his confidence in their rescuers.

Roger Chapman is a modest man, and writes modestly about his own achievement, but Roger Mallinson, his companion, gave Roger Chapman enormous credit for his boundless courage.

There was no giving way to the deep urge to sleep, but what a gigantic effort it must have been to drag himself out of it for the essential job of working the life support systems.

How does one describe the quiet heroism and quality of men, sealed in their tiny craft for over 80 hours, finally rescued with the odds well against them, who continue to go on diving again?

Words seem superfluous to describe men of such metal.

# 1. Crash Dive

The first few days of a new charter were always hectic after returning from 'stand down', those few days of rest between jobs. At home it had been trying to unwind, doing a few jobs around the house, talking to wives and friends, and attempting not to talk shop too often. If the stand down was very short I could never quite unwind fully, so it felt good to be on the job again, off to Scotland in the middle of the night, recklessly driving far too fast, the car crammed with men and diving suits as the stereo blazed. One's wife left at home must be wondering if you had really been home at all.

However, this time the trip was not Scotland but Ireland. We were to work on a charter for the British Post Office, which was something different. The mother ship *Vickers Voyager*, with our mini submersible *Pisces III* aboard, was already working far out in the Atlantic, 150 miles off Cork in Southern Ireland. The job involved burying a section of underwater armoured telephone cable, part of a transatlantic line called Cantat 2, stretching across 3,230 miles of ocean between Widemouth Bay in Cornwall and Beaver Harbour in Nova Scotia. Cantat 2 would be able to carry 1,840 simultaneous telephone

*The mother ship* Vickers Voyager *with her mini submersible* Pisces III *suspended from the heavy frame at the stern.*

conversations, which is more than all the other existing transatlantic cables combined.

Trawlermen are fishing deeper and deeper as the demand for food increases, so today their trawls may go down to depths of almost a mile to bring in creatures which are strange looking, but good food all the same—especially when covered in batter. It is unfortunate for the trawlermen if their nets catch hold of a submarine cable; however a large heave can break the cable to free their nets and so let the fishing continue. Yet this can be disastrous to the men of the Post Office in England and the Canadian Overseas Telecommunications Corporation. The £30M cable followed three years of careful planning and research: then laying it took six months by three ships, including the ice-breaker cable layer, *John Cabot*, which later played such a vital role in the story to follow.

Our job with the two-man submersible *Pisces III* was to bury this important cable at least one foot below the mud on the ocean floor throughout the area where the trawlermen might be working. It was to be a long job, working steadily out to the west along the Continental Shelf at less than 2 m.p.h. on the sea-bed, gradually descending to 3,000 ft. Three thousand feet was our maximum operating depth on this charter, but across the Atlantic at the other end of Cantat 2 and working her way eastwards on the same job of cable burying, was *Pisces V*, a mini-sub of the same class, but she was capable of operating down to 6,000 feet below the sea surface.

The *Voyager* and *Pisces III* had worked for three weeks with the first team of pilots and divers, led by Bob Hanley. Fair weather had allowed good progress and new devices were being tried out to make cable

*Our job was to bury the Cantat 2 cable stretching 3,230 miles across the Atlantic, so that*

burial more efficient. After twenty days of diving night and day they were all glad to be back in Cork for a rest and change-round of submersible teams.

I was one of a team of pilots and divers flying to Cork to join the *Voyager* and continue the job of burying the Cantat 2 cable. We were a mixed bunch: David Mayo and myself, were both ex-lieutenants of the Royal Navy, invalided out of the service due to poor eyesight and now submersible pilots; then Roger Mallinson, the third pilot, was an engineer by trade who lived in his own special world and made miniature steam engines as a hobby. In all there were eight of us in the team, ably led by Ralph Henderson, who had joined Oceanics at its outset, and had become an experienced Field Officer.

Tiredness began to set in from the very first evening. The submersible was in need of a great deal of

*fishing trawls would not damage it.*

maintenance, but inevitably we all went drinking together that first night *Voyager* was in port. For the team joining, thoughts of the work required of us were uppermost in our minds; while the team leaving were happy to relax and drink as we all crammed into the corner of an Irish bar, trying not to sound too English. The times were hard in Ireland, even in the south; we were approached by a serious bearded young man asking us to subscribe to the IRA in the north.

We drank too much beer but learnt much about the job at hand. *Pisces III* had already worked down to 1,400 feet and at the point she had reached on the last dive had left a sonic beacon, called a pinger, to tell us where we had to continue the cable burying. The nature of the seabed was soft sand so it was easy to work and provided good conditions for cable burial.

The food aboard *Voyager* was tasty and the men from the Post Office working with us on this charter formed a cheerful and efficient team; so conditions were as good as could be expected. Most of us would be diving and working in *Pisces III* deeper than we had ever been before and several beers later we were looking forward to the charter!

The next day I was not so sure. The main problems with the submersible were electrical; Irish beer is strong and a dull headache remained as the team investigated poor insulation readings on the motors. Towards noon on that day, August 25th, 1973, we found it necessary to remove one motor completely and start taking it apart. Meanwhile, almost unnoticed, the ship sailed out of Cork, making her way down river through the picturesque scenery in bright sunlight, then out to sea. Work went on all afternoon and into the night. *Voyager* steered for the point in the ocean where 1,400 feet below a section of telephone cable was exposed on the seabed as it stretched out from one continent to another.

It was fortunate that we had some time on board before starting the first dive, for it was not until late the following day, as *Voyager* approached the position, that *PIII* was at last resembling an operational submersible. The weather had been rough on the way out, and the team was weary. Roger Mallinson had been seasick part of the time and because he was the most experienced engineer and maintainer on board, repairs had taken longer than usual. Ralph, as Field Officer, decided that with the poor weather and crew fatigue, diving would not start until the following morning.

That evening, after a splendid meal, we all watched a film but we had to hang on to the projector as the ship was rolling about in the heavy seas. Then we had a few beers and went to bed, hoping for better operating conditions the next day.

Diving began the following morning as planned and as the weather had improved I felt that time would fly with three weeks non-stop work ahead, operating day and night. If the weather held, there would be no break in the routine; it would be dive, up again, fix the submersible, de-brief, eat and then sleep, whilst the batteries of *PIII* were re-charged; then the whole sequence would begin again. The Post Office was paying a good deal for our services and fine weather was too good to waste.

The first dive lasted nine hours. The second lasted only two hours as we never reached the bottom; this

| DATE | DETAILS OF DIVING OPERATIONS | DEPTH IN FEET | DURA-TION IN MINS. | EQUIP-MENT USED |
|---|---|---|---|---|
| | G. P.O. CHARTER   23 Aug 1973 — Sat 1st Sept. | | | |
| 27/8 | DIVE ② Pilot Self | | | |
| | Obs David Mayo | | | |
| | Location Western Approaches ℃ 2M SW | | | |
| | Islands | 1380' | 2 Hrs | I Ⅲ |
| | Deeper yet! but we never reached the bottom. | | | |
| | Line broke when we could just see bottom on | | | |
| | E/s at 20'. Very frustrating. Long recovery | | | |
| | because of bad conditions. And skin topside was | | | |
| | very ill (DIVER) | | | |
| | Rough WEATHER PM   No DIVE. | | | |
| 28/8 | DIVE ③ Pilot Self   Obs D. Mayo. | | | |
| | Location as above. | 1650' | 8½ Hrs | P Ⅲ |
| 0700 | Deeper! Cable break from Nelson buoy point deeper. | | | |
| | bottom. Soft Sand / Mud | | | |
| 1600. | Vis 15' Lts on | | | |
| | Conditions. Good / No Tide | | 70½ | |

*Part of Roger Chapman's personal diving log showing that he had 70½ hours experience in mini submersibles before the dive which through accident was to more than double this time.*

was because our marker buoy line broke when we were approaching the seabed with only 20 feet to go. It was my first dive that trip as pilot, so a disappointment, but it was the deepest I had been underwater, which gave it interest. By the time we had returned to the surface the weather had become so bad that we had to be recovered. I went down again as the pilot on the third dive, which lasted 8½ hours and brought us back to the routine.

We went down again on Dive 4 with Roger as pilot and I as the observer. We had little or no sleep before the dive, as a technical hitch had kept us up most of the night. By that Wednesday morning, August 29, we were worn out as we approached the surface after another nine hours on the seabed, hungry and damp from the humidity inside the tiny sphere. We reeled around while the towline was attached by a diver outside with *PIII* bobbing up and down in the waves; then began the haul up to the stern of *Voyager* for recovery.

*The haul up to the stern of the mother ship for recovery, going stern first with a diver clinging to the sail.*

Sometimes during recovery the water alarm sounded, triggered off by the condensation in the aft sphere, where equipment and oil are housed. So when the alarm sounded we thought little of it at first; but when it sounded for a second time—ringing continuously, accompanied by a rasping noise echoing inside our own sphere—, we were thoroughly alerted, although still not certain whether it was an electrical fault or a real alarm.

Three seconds later we realised that the alarm was real. Voices could be heard shouting over our VHF radio. Roger and I, totally confused, sat looking at each other, motionless.

'There must be condensation in the aft sphere' I said and then 'What the hell is happening now'. The submersible tipped backwards 45 degrees. There was a rushing noise. The wretched water alarm was still blaring away.

Roger, pinned at the back of the sphere and trying to clamber to the controls, suddenly noticed the depth gauge. 'Look at the bloody depth'. I was horrified to see the needle was past 100 feet and moving downwards. We had no idea what was happening as seconds before we had been safely on the surface under tow and we had no means of seeing what had gone on at the top of the submersible.

When 175 feet down a chaotic nightmare began. The towline, still attached to our stern, abruptly halted the rapid descent. We might have been inside a crazy big dipper as the ship tossed up and down on the surface, jerking us about like a fish caught by the tail. Pieces of equipment were flying around us as we tried to hang on; we wanted to do something about it, but there was absolutely nothing we could do to help ourselves in that turmoil except to avoid the sonar set which came crashing out of its bracket.

We heard more voices, but this time they came from the under water telephone instead of from the radio. Then Roger was yelling into the microphone, while I felt sick. The whole world had gone mad. I just desperately wanted to get the hell out of that tiny sphere.

The sheer helplessness, combined with the non-stop violence of the movement, was an outrage to my whole way of life and upbringing. Through the years I had been taught to act positively in emergencies, especially under the sea. Yet there was nothing I could do, and I was being thrown about with a brutal force I had never experienced before.

Why on earth should I be stuck in a tiny steel sphere, far below the sea surface, getting thrown around like a rat in a terrier's mouth.

How had my life led me to this?

# 2. Early Days

The first time I saw a submarine was at the age of 15. Six schoolboys, from various parts of the country and with differing backgrounds, had assembled at Gosport in Hampshire for our interview to join the Royal Navy. I am sure none of this group of six knew for certain why he wanted to join the Navy, but we all had the stock answers ready for the gruelling half hour sessions, when I felt that I was being glared at by the very senior and austere men in blue, each with an array of gold braid on his arms. Intermingled with the interviews and intelligence tests were initiative tests, forms to fill in, and perhaps worst of all was waiting for the next ordeal. The whole business was truly alarming to a 15-year old.

The Navy, in its wisdom, sensed that maybe this was a bit much for a young man who was offering his services to Queen and country for fourteen bob a day; so during the first evening of the two-day session it arranged a visit in a nautical atmosphere to take the strain off the proceedings. I still had the niggling suspicion that we were being watched, and should be continually asking more intelligent questions on lengths, breadths, and tonnage from the chief petty officer—he seemed to me at least a hundred years old—who accompanied us in the bus. However, I kept quiet, but in every group there is always a leader and our group of six was no exception. A large lad ventured the only question on the way to the submarine base at HMS Dolphin. 'We'll have time for a pint, Chief, won't we?'

This must have been something out of the norm for the chief petty officer; he must have realised over the ages that rather nervous young gentlemen attending admiralty interviews straight from school were unlikely to show any common sense whatsoever. He recovered his cool in a split second and promptly stopped the bus at the next pub.

At 15 we all felt ourselves hardened drinkers and the chief, still in a good mood, stood us each a pint; this was about ¾ pint more beer than I had ever previously drunk in one sitting, and as the bus continued to HMS Dolphin all fears of hidden eyes and ears disappeared, while I even wondered bravely whether there might be time for a pint or two on the way back.

Anyway, back to the submarine. In 1960, which was the year of my interview, the submarine service had just begun a period of growth which continued to the day I write this; so perhaps this visit to the home of the British Submarine Command was a tactical move to sow the seeds in budding 'U'-boat commanders. Our little group probably did not produce a good return: indeed ten minutes after disappearing below into HMS Totem, an old T-class conversion conventional submarine, the big lad who led us astray was violently sick. I nearly followed his lead, but just managed to break back into fresh air in time.

So, in all honesty, my memory of that first submarine is a little hazy. All I can remember is that the compartments looked incredibly small and cramped, while there was a strong smell of fuel oil. At the time we put this down to the fact that the particular submarine had been out of commission for some time; but as submariners will know, all diesel driven submarines have this distinct smell, which clings to clothes and personal belongings long after you leave the confines of the hull.

Two and a half years later, in 1963, I joined the Royal Navy at Dartmouth. In my second year of training I was very fortunate to voyage in a frigate to the Far East, and during this time the ship paid several visits to Hong Kong. It was on the last visit that I came into close contact with my second submarine. Specialist submarine training was only given to commissioned officers after the initial four years of general training; but much of this training had already been teaching me how submarines are hunted down and sunk, as the destruction of enemy submarines is one of the primary tasks of our island fleet. Thus I was curious to find out what the other side of the picture felt like and wanted to go below the sea.

In Hong Kong our anti-submarine frigate berthed near to the submarine HMS *Anchorite*, the 'enemy' during exercises in the China Sea, and indeed the 'enemy' for an assortment of ships to practise hunting. On impulse more than anything else I managed to find my way down to the submarine's minute wardroom—a small boxlike compartment where the officers ate, played cards and worked when not on watch; there I asked the first lieutenant if there was any chance of me going to sea in the submarine for the trip to Singapore.

As I was a midshipman I thought it unlikely that permission would be given, but by good luck one of the submarine's officers had flown to Singapore, so there was room for a passenger. I had no idea what 'room' meant, as the wardroom was already incredibly overcrowded, even with the majority of the officers still ashore savouring the delights of Kowloon, which is perhaps the Soho of Hong Kong.

From the time of this first sea trip in a submarine there was never any doubt in my mind that I wanted to specialise in the submarine service—not that we even dived below the surface on that five day voyage to Singapore. However, once inside the hull, with all the hatches shut, it is much the same whether on the surface or underwater; the main difference is that cruising on the surface fresh air is being sucked down through the conning tower, which is the only access to the outside world, by the hungry diesels as they clatter away charging up the batteries which drive the propellers. When dived, the conning tower hatch is tight shut, and then the batteries' reserve of power drives the propellers without the accompaniment of diesels, which can only work with a plentiful supply of air.

Air is the submariner's major problem, whether its a large submarine carrying some 200 men, or a two-man submersible like *Pisces III*.

When dived a constant eye must be kept on the state of the atmosphere. Every time a man breathes out he is exhaling carbon dioxide, a poison gas which will build up to a dangerous concentration unless removed. The limit generally accepted for carbon dioxide is 2% of the atmosphere for an extended period: however as soon as the proportion reaches 0.5%, steps should be taken to start removing it, as otherwise headaches begin, then an increasing percentage of carbon dioxide leads to nausea and eventually death.

In a large submarine, such as *HMS Anchorite*, carbon dioxide very seldom gets as high as 0.5%, as the batteries must be recharged when power is used by the propellers; this means coming to the surface to drive the diesels, thus replenishing the air for the crew. Things are different in a tiny submersible as I was to find out later.

Certainly my first voyage from Hong Kong to Singapore made me impatient to start submarine training for real. In a disciplined service such as the Royal Navy, one of the biggest attractions of submarines is the apparently relaxed atmosphere once at sea, combined with the general respect officers and men have for each other while living and working together in confined spaces. Along with this relaxed atmosphere goes a sense of real responsibility and technical know-how: every man, whether he be a cook or the captain, is genuinely capable of endangering the lives of his fellows by even some simple error, and this leads to mutual respect as long as you all remain alive. All this is built round a particular sense of humour that the average submariner seems to acquire: it is a humour that the outsider sometimes finds difficult to understand.

One outsider I remember distinctly being taken aback by submarine humour was an admiral visiting our submarine which had been berthed alongside a wharf for his inspection. An engine room mechanic had spent the previous day painstakingly repairing a fuel separator and had been forced to stop work and clear up his oily mess for the inspection to take place. As the admiral stepped through the narrow hatch into the engine room he asked the sailor in a true British naval voice 'And what do you do, my man'. 'Well Sir', came the reply. 'As soon as you have gone I can get on with my work, stripping down this f....... separator'.

Having completed training in the submarine school at HMS Dolphin, I spent the next $3\frac{1}{2}$ to 4 years in conventional submarines, mainly east of Suez. Everything was going well with my career and in 1971 I was posted to Barrow-in-Furness on the north-west coast of England to join *HMS Swiftsure*, a new nuclear submarine which was being built by the famous firm of shipbuilders, Vickers Limited. Barrow is close to the Lake District, a wonderful part of the world to live in, so a posting to *HMS Swiftsure* at Barrow was thoroughly popular for most of the crew, especially those with family ties, as it would be several months before she would be ready to sail for seatrials.

Vickers had been building submarines for the British and other navies throughout many years, and its reputation as a shipbuilder was second to none. In recent years it had completed two nuclear Polaris class submarines, so it seems natural that the building of *HMS Swiftsure*, as the first of a class of hunter-killer nuclear submarines, should also be entrusted to Vickers.

The completion of such a very sophisticated and complicated vessel could not be rushed, but my task as navigator did not need so much time: thus I became restless, but by chance a temporary outlet came with the illness of the navigator in another ship. She was a nuclear submarine which had been built by Vickers two years before, and she was at sea engaged in an intensive operational programme; a few telephone calls between the two commanding officers and I was off out of the Lake District and back to sea for two months.

This period proved to be a turning point in my naval career. At the end of the two months, I was doubtful whether my eyesight was up to the standard required to navigate deep draught vessels in shallow waters. For some years I had been suffering from very slight shortsightedness and had noticed a deterioration, so it was with reluctance that I presented myself for a check and certainly I did not then realise that this would lead eventually to being invalided out of the Navy. The check showed that without glasses my eyesight was not good against the standard set by the Royal Navy for submarine duty, which requires almost perfect vision. After further checks, I was faced with a choice. Either I could return to the surface fleet, with further annual check-ups and the prospect of being invalided out of the navy should there be further deterioration, as I was already on the borderline; or alternatively I could leave straightaway and embark on a new career in the outside world.

It was with great reluctance that I chose to leave the Royal Navy, as I had enjoyed many happy years in it.

*The nuclear submarine* HMS Swiftsure *being launched at Barrow.*

Returning to Barrow and *HMS Swiftsure*, the wheels were put in motion for me to leave the navy. A relief could not be found in a hurry, which gave me time to look around for a job outside in civvy street; after many trips to London and elsewhere I found the ideal solution just 300 yards from where *HMS Swiftsure* was lying.

Vickers Oceanics, an offshoot of the parent company Vickers, had started operating commercially two new submersibles of the Pisces class, and was looking for men to train as pilots. It was too good to be true. Peter Messervy, a retired Royal Navy commander who was the general manager of Oceanics, interviewed me and I explained my problem; the next thing was that I was offered a job which I could take up when released from HMS *Swiftsure*. I would not even have to move away from Barrow or leave the sea.

My last three months in the navy were probably the most interesting and rewarding. *HMS Swiftsure*, all gleaming and new, was ready for seatrials. Vickers had taken exceptional care in completing her, as she was to dive deeper than any other submarine then built for service with the Royal Navy. With the ever watchful eyes and intense effort of the engineers who built her, followed by those who took her through her trials, *Swiftsure* ran deeper and deeper, going faster and faster. All went without a hitch and she emerged from her trials in first class order.

Towards the end of her trial I returned to Barrow one weekend, having handed over to my relief. I felt confident in joining Vickers Oceanics, who in just a few years had become specialists in their own field. Certainly it was not speed over the seabed that they were hoping to achieve, but the aim was to enable men to work at great depths with all the fascination of life under the sea. The disappointment of leaving my career in the Royal Navy was certainly lessened by the prospect of returning underwater with a difference.

# 3. Two-man Submersibles

Before we continue further into the story of the deepest submarine rescue in history, I must first describe the fascinating process of how two-man submersibles are operated.

The urgent need for underwater work, for instance with the oil rigs in the North Sea, often means that a man with specialised techniques may have to go to the seabottom. He may not be fully trained as a diver or even medically fit, and divers who work at great depths in their individual suits face quite a risk to their immediate safety, quite apart from the possible

*The author inside the sphere of a two-man submersible looking out through the pilot's port when on the mother ship's deck.*

# PISCES III

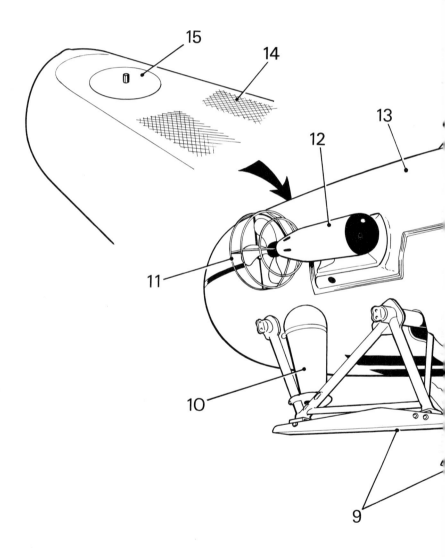

15

14

13

12

11

10

9

1  Sail
2  High Powered Lights
3  Pinger Receiver
4  Sonar Dome
5  View Ports
6  Nozzle for burying
   cable
7  Manipulator Assembly

8  Drop Weight
9  Skids
10 High Pressure Air
11 Propeller Guard
12 Electric Motor
13 GRP Skin
14 Deck Treads
15 Aft Hatch

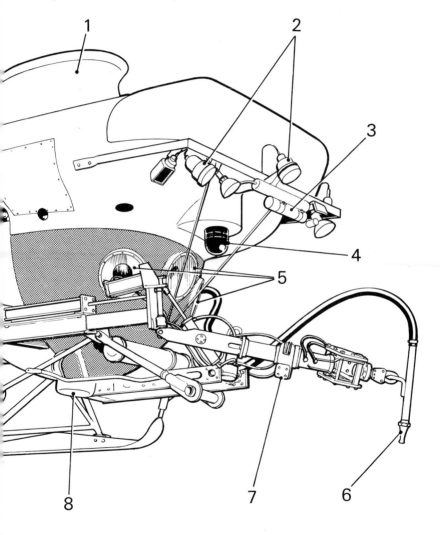

lasting effects of underwater illnesses such as bone neucrosis.

A submersible pilot however, is not subject to the extreme pressures that a diver must endure when he is working underwater. Once his hatch is shut, the pressure inside his small spherical world remains much the same as the outside air, even though he may be working at great depths.

The inside of a submersible is just like being in a very small lift or elevator with curved walls of steel, and an access hatch immediately above your head like a trap door to the top of the lift. The bottom of the round steel sphere has a wooden deck, under which there is a mass of pipes and small pumps; however these do not normally need to be seen or operated by the pilot any more than the water pipes and electric leads under the floorboards at his home. If we start then with this floor hatch, there is just room to stand up with head bent, when the hatch is shut.

For the pilots to sit, or half lie down, two curved wooden benches are placed round the sides of the sphere, facing the three ports, which are small round windows made of special material to withstand extreme pressure. Through these, half lying and peering out into the gloom of the seabed, a pilot can view the fascination of another world. The creatures of the other world swim up to the ports, attracted by the bright lights, and take a look inside. They are unafraid and undisturbed, as once underwater the submersible quickly becomes part of the environment.

Perhaps this is digressing a little, but the underworld quickly captures the imagination with its endless surprises and fascination. Going back to picture our sphere, under the benches more equipment and valves are hidden, and then the various controls are fixed in every available space elsewhere around the steel walls.

First of these is the pilot's console. It may look a complex mass of gauges and valves, but really it is very straightforward. There are controls for two small electric motors which are attached to the outside casing and filled with oil; by simply increasing the drive on one motor more than the other, the pilot steers his submersible, as there is no rudder in the Pisces class submersible. We can lie down in comfort and direct our sphere over the seabed, above which it stands on

*Working on the crew sphere of* Pisces III *with the fibreglass casing stripped off. At the top is the trim sphere.*

skids, looking like large skis. So that the submersible can move with ease over the softest of mud it must be capable of skimming over the seafloor without sticking in the soft ooze. We need a fine degree of 'trim', which is the word we use for adjusting the bodily weight of the vessel in the water. A human being does it automatically—it is easy to dive down to the bottom of the swimming pool, swim around and then come up again for air. In a submersible, all that is required is to open a small vent or air hole on top of a tank, which allows the pressure of the sea to force water into this tank. The vent is operated electrically from within, and as soon as the pilot feels the submersible becoming heavier, he shuts the vent. However at great depths, such as with our job in the Atlantic for the Post Office, the sea pressure might be as much as a thousand pounds per square inch and the water would be forced in so fast that a fraction of a second might be too long for the adjustment needed. So at great depths there is another system which enables the pilot to have a finer control over his trim. This is done by pumping oil from inside the submersible into rubber bags situated outside which become buoyant or light because the oil is lighter than seawater. This trimming oil when inside is kept in a separate large sphere behind the pilot sphere, and throughout the book this is known as the aft sphere.

*Pisces III*'s aft sphere is the principle rogue in this story, as the hatch to it was suddenly torn off accidentally minutes before we were to be hoisted back safely on deck; water poured in, and *Pisces III* became like a rock weighing a ton or more in the water, so fell to the seabed. However we are rushing on a little, there is something more to learn before we move onto the action, and incidentally the name *Pisces III* is often abbreviated to PIII.

Thus the submersible can be made by its crew to dive up and down or to move along the ocean floor. Below about 200 feet, even on a bright day, it is pitch dark; light normally detectable by the human eye can scarcely penetrate any further. So outside the sphere three bright lights shine down from a bar above the ports, and depending on the clarity of the water, they usually give plenty of light to work and observe.

All the submersible needs now is some equipment to locate objects on the seabed, and then some tools to work with. With all these it becomes a viable commercial machine as well as an interesting observation vehicle; but everything has to be as compact and light as possible.

The small sonar set sends a beam of sound out into the sea, and when it hits an object the beam bounces back and records on a screen the direction and distance. This gives the pilot his search capability, but some of the practical difficulties of operating sonar, perhaps when searching for a sunken submersible, come later in the story. The sea distorts sound in a peculiar way, bending it up and down; this largely depends upon temperature gradients, but is often unpredictable.

Once the object of the search is successfully shown on the screen, a gyro compass gives the true direction in which to move off. If you are looking for something deep down, nine times out of the ten the submersible is moved off towards it with great caution, particularly if it is a large shape. Here again is a certain fascination as it is still the world of the relatively unknown. Some objects which appear as large as life on the sonar may suddenly disappear; then if you are looking for a lost anchor you may discover that the object on the screen which you think is the anchor turns out to be a rock a hundred times bigger. When looking for *PIII* with Roger and I trapped in her the crew of *PV* played this game of searching and not finding for hours on end.

Once a submersible is launched from the mother ship it acts as a completely independent unit. The only visible link is a thin nylon line and attached to it is a large orange marker buoy, which bobs up and down on the surface showing the approximate position of the submersible beneath; that is unless the line has been taken off at the end of a dive, as was the case with *PIII* when she sank. The support ship hovers around this buoy and every fifteen minutes carries out a communications check with the submersible below. The pilots answer and pass

*Communications system showing the microphone through which the pilots speak to those on on the surface.*

any other information through the submarine telephone; rough conditions can play tricks with the sound and occasionally neither can hear the other. Again dolphins may make such a noise that they interrupt communications.

When the submersible is on the surface communication between it and the ship is by radio, which is particularly important for launch and recovery operations; but the radio is no use with the submersible dived.

With two men breathing out in a steel sphere only 80 inches in diameter, the carbon dioxide level quickly gets above 0.5%, and every 30 minutes or so it must be reduced by a process known as scrubbing.

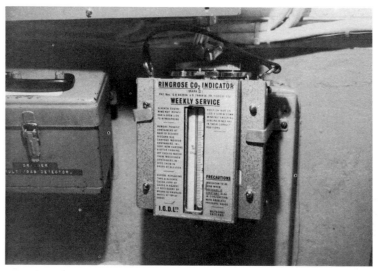

*The Ringrose indicator which constantly tells the pilots the percentage of carbon dioxide in the atmosphere of the crew sphere.*

This is done by a small electric fan dragging the stale air through a canister of lithium hydroxide, which removes the poisonous carbon dioxide. The fan is no bigger than a one pound tin of boiled sweets, and the whole process lowers the pressure in the sphere slightly, which leaves room for more oxygen to be added.

Under normal working conditions in a Pisces class submersible the crew will consume oxygen at the rate of about one

*The carbon dioxide scrubber motor with a lithium hydroxide canister in position above it, surrounded by spare canisters and oxygen.*

litre each man every minute, written as 1 litre/min/man. To replace this, spare gaseous oxygen is carried in two cylinders, each of 63 cubic feet capacity and capable of taking a pressure of 3,000 lbs/in$^2$.

*An oxygen cylinder clamped to the side of the sphere in Pisces showing the gauge approaching zero.*

Under these average working conditions scrubbing might take from ten to fifteen minutes to get the carbon dioxide down to an acceptable level, then oxygen from a cylinder is slowly bled into the air through a small valve until the pressure in back to atmospheric,—that is the air pressure of the outside world on the surface.

If everything else is operating properly, the oxygen from the two full cylinders carried should last two men for about 30 hours at a consumption of 1 litre/min/man,—say just over a day. By lying down and doing as little as possible the oxygen consumption can be kept down to $\frac{1}{2}$ litre/min/man, and then the supply will last twice as long. Indeed Pisces operators were trained that should an accident leave them stranded on the

sea bottom, the rescue organisation would rely on the crew to use as little oxygen as possible, aiming to last out for about 72 hours, or 3 days.

Then come the tools with which to work underwater, and these vary with the particular job involved. For the Post Office charter our main task was to bury cable, so a special mud pump was fitted which blasted a jet of sea water at the soft mud on the seabed, digging a trench into which the cable dropped. The passage of time does the rest of the work as the trench fills in by itself during the weeks and months ahead, thus covering the precious cable. To direct this jet exactly at the correct place it is held in position by a manipulator or mechanical arm, just like having outside a human arm which

Pisces III

*The manipulator, or mechanical arm, is operated from within the sphere to twist, bend up and down or pick things up.*

can twist, bend up and down, or pick things up. This is probably the most important tool ever carried and is absolutely essential for rescue work; indeed without a manipulator a submersible is very restricted.

Cameras, which tilt up and down, record on video tape so that a picture of all the work done on the dive can be shown to anyone interested when the submersible is back on deck.

Launch and recovery can be tricky parts of operations, although in absolutely calm conditions there is no problem. A large lift line picks the submersible up off the deck at the stern of the ship; then the lift line is lowered away to release the submersible just above the water. Simple.

A diver who is already standing on the submersible casing disconnects the lift line and the ship slowly tows the little craft, half submerged and ready to disappear beneath the waves, into the exact pre-planned position. There the towline is released by the diver, who swims underwater to release a small

*Recovery of Pisces is no problem in calm conditions as seen on the right. The full recovery sequence is shown on pages 38–41.*

*Approaching the stern of the submersible is the Gemini dragging a towline, while with hand raised in the water is the diver.*

*The towline is connected and Pisces.*

**Typical recovery sequence of a mini submersible in moderate weather conditions.**

*swims round to climb onboard*

Pisces *is towed by the support ship to a position under the hook. It was during this phase that the towline of* Pisces III *became entangled round the aft sphere locking mechanism.*

41

These photos continue a typical recovery sequence on a mini submersible. They actually show *Pisces II* and on that occasion Roger Chapman was the pilot.

*Pisces is lifted clear of the water.*

*The diver connects the lift hook.*

*A safety strop is secured.*

*Close up of the lift hook.*

43

*The Gemini, seen as it is lowered over the side of* Voyager, *acts as attendant to the mini submarine at launch and recovery whatever the weather.*

hook. Finally the light marker buoy is attached, and as the submersible rapidly disappears below the waves the buoy's line is paid out from the attendant rubber boat, called the Gemini.

When the weather is rough, the procedure is the same, but everything is just that much more difficult. The diver has to hang on with one arm or leg whilst disconnecting the lift line; then he must judge the exact time to enter the water to disconnect the tow as the waves wash completely over him and the submersible. Meanwhile the Gemini is being thrown about, depending on the strength of the wind, so generally everyone is very relieved when the launch is successfully carried out. The pilots inside the sphere are OK, though the violent motion on the surface often leads to sea sickness among those who are prone to it. If one of you is sick at the beginning of a dive, the next eight hours can be pretty foul.

What makes a man then, curled up in a cramped position for eight hours, in dim light and stuffy humid conditions, often in the middle of the night and feeling tired, earn a living in this way?

Many people have asked me this question since our unfortunate episode; but after six months right away from the sea, I have been quietly drawn back. In my case I can put it down to the past, I think. I had spent six years in the Navy, in submarines, but never once actually saw what was outside when underwater. Then suddenly with Vickers Oceanics and *Pisces*, there was the seabed. Whether at 150 feet or 1,500 feet there is always something to look at; yet each dive is different. Very quickly the unpleasant side of life is forgotten, even the immediate atmospheric conditions inside the sphere, with the humidity rising rapidly to 100% become tolerable. An eight hour dive passes quickly and it is only during the ascent that you feel like getting out into the fresh air.

In Oceanics we were given a good training. Before passing out as a qualified pilot, every other job in the team had to be undertaken many times. This meant operating the lift lines and handling gear, carrying out the maintenance and dive checks, driving the rubber Gemini in all conditions, while some trainee pilots had practice in the duties of the diver. Complete confidence is built up in a team very quickly and each of the eight men operating the submersible gets to know each other very well.

Well, there it is. A ship, a submersible and a bunch of guys with a job to do, perhaps at 1,500 feet or even 3,000 feet. This time something was to go horribly wrong; it was an accident that could not possibly have been foreseen and was no-one's fault.

Two of us in the team were to spend 84 hours crammed together. We came from completely different walks of life and had many different interests so that if we had not worked together, we would probably never have struck up a friendship. This account of what happened is dedicated to the men who struggled without sleep, and used every resource and professional skill, to get us safely to the surface.

# 4. Dive 325

By Tuesday night I was feeling pretty tired but luckily did not have to get *Pisces III* ready for the next dive because Roger Mallinson had been nominated as pilot; it was to be *PIII's* dive no 325. There were still two or three fellows working around her; the main problem was that the manipulator was not behaving as it should, and this meant it had to be stripped down. Roger M. was inside still working away, occasionally operating the manipulator as requested by the maintainers outside and also getting everything ready for the dive.

It must have been around this time that a voice inside him was saying 'change the main oxygen bottle', This bottle had about 700 pounds per square inch (psi) remaining from my last dive, which would have been enough for an eight hour dive, assuming the normal consumption of half a litre each per man. Often one dived without replacing the in-use oxygen cylinder, but this was not recommended practice; however with the reserve bottle reading 2900 psi it would have been so easy to disregard this basic pre-dive requirement and dive without both oxygen bottles fully charged. As it turned out the voice telling Roger to change the bottle made all the difference to the rescue operation and perhaps our survival.

Roger must have been very tired by then working in the hot and uncomfortable atmosphere inside *Pisces*. Oxygen bottles are awkward to change as they are held to the inside of the command sphere by clips, and like everything else inside the submersible, they are just too large to move around easily.

It is a strange thing at night how a ship goes to sleep. At about 10 or 11 o'clock people are just beginning to turn in. The weather may not change, but somehow the ship becomes quiet and almost appears to settle on a steady course for the night. But when you are working and know that you may have to get up for the next watch or you have another dive to do in the middle of the night, you still cannot help feeling sleepy as the ship does. It must have been about 11 o'clock that I poked my head inside *Pisces*, and shouted down to Roger asking how he was getting on. I mentioned that he really ought to get some sleep as we had a long night ahead of us. However, Roger, just as in everything else he does or gets involved in, wanted to make sure that his boat was all set to dive before turning in. He was going to stick with the problem of the manipulator until it was repaired. I wandered off, had a cup of coffee in the galley and then went off to my bunk.

It seemed like the next minute that I was given a shake and told it was time to get up; I suppose it was not very long, perhaps a couple of hours. I dressed in trousers and a shirt, with overalls on top. Because it was humid in *Voyager* and the cabins were quite hot, I did not put on a sweater, but during the three and a half day rescue I certainly had ample cause to regret this. Normally one should either wear a sweater or take it in the submersible just in case of emergency, but after many routine dives, these little things tend to get neglected.

Thus, rather inadequately clothed, I wandered back towards *Pisces* and found to my surprise that work was still going on around the boat although she was due to dive in about half an hour. Roger was apparently still working, although he had slept for a few minutes during the night, and obviously the problem had taken longer than expected. The batteries, however, had been charged and the support ship was moving into position for the launch. The manipulator was in the last stages of re-assembly and as this was a charter that involved a great deal of important work, it was critical that we kept to our timetable. If *Pisces* could be got ready to dive on time, then her crew must be ready to do the work.

Collection of our rations is a standard practice before a dive; they generally consist of the sandwiches one liked, which had been ordered earlier from the galley. Probably I ordered cheese and chutney, while Roger ordered his choice. We also had some fresh fruit which always came cold out of the fridge—it was apples and oranges this time; then there was a flask of coffee, a carton of milk and sugar.

About 1.30 am everything was ready at last and we were sitting in the boat waiting for a normal launch. We were going back down to the cable where I had deployed the pinger the dive before. As soon as you are inside the boat and sitting down it is as though you are in another world, even though your craft is still on the deck of the support ship, you know that this will be your environment for the next eight to ten hours, so very quickly, with the familiar tools of your trade and the familiar sounds coming over the radio, you get into a mental routine, although for some time before the launch the hatch is still open.

All the pre-dive routines have been completed by this time but there would still be a few you must check once more; you check communications on the VHF radio; you may check your lights; you check little things like a handy pencil for writing out the log, and special things such as enough video tape for the duration of the dive; then you make sure that everything is fully secured just in case you meet rough weather on the surface.

*Part of* Pisces III *check list for Dive 325.*

| PRE-DIVE CHECKS | DIVE No.:- 325 | | DATE:- 29·8·73 | |
|---|---|---|---|---|
| EXTERNALLY ENSURE:- | | DROP WEIGHT WRENCH | | ✓ |
| | | JETTISON OIL RESERVOIR TOPPED | | ✓ |
| ALL EQUIPMENT SECURED | ✓ | " OPERATING LEVER FITTED | | ✓ |
| PORTS CLEANED | ✓ | T V SYSTEM FUNCTIONING | | ✓ |
| EMER'cy BUOY RELEASE WORKING | ✓ | SPARE VIDEO TAPES CARRIED | | ✓ |
| " " LINE LENGTH = MAX DEPTH | ✓ | JETTISON & EMERG'cy BUOY VALVES SHUT | | ✓ |
| COMP. BAGS. PROP. MOTORS. MANIP'tor & SONAR 2/3rds FULL | ✓ | MANIP'tor RELEASE COMP. VALVES SHUT OPEN | | ✓ |
| PHYSICALLY CHECK AFT SPHERE | ✓ | CABIN VENT VALVE SHUT | | ✓ |
| HATCH & VENT PLUG SECURED | ✓ | CHECK POWER TO:- | | |
| MAIN HATCH O-RING CLEANED & GREASED | ✓ | SONAR ✓ | GYRO | ✓ |
| BATT. OIL TOPPED AT 0035 Hrs | | ECHO SOUNDER ✓ | PINGER LOCATOR | ✓ |
| " RESERVOIR PLUG SECURED | ✓ | AIR SCRUBBER ✓ | D.C.-A.C. INVERTER | ✓ |
| INTERNAL H.P. AIR | | Hyd. Pump 1700p.s.i ✓ | JABSCO | ✓ |
| BATT. VOLTS. 2 x PSI 3400 / 2 x PSI 3400 | | EXTERNAL LIGHTS ✓ | INTERNAL LIGHTS | ✓ |
| 120v 132v | | VENT VALVES ✓ | Water Ind.(Fielden) | ✓ |
| 24v 27v OXYGEN MAIN 3000 RESERVE 2900 | | V.H.F. RADIO ✓ | U.W.T. UP & DOWN | ✓ |
| 12v 12·6 LIOH. HOURS 2 RESERVE ✓ | | OPERATE EMERGENCY TRIP & CONFIRM | | ✓ |
| 12v EMG'cy ✓ USED 18hrs + FILTERS ✓ | | 12v EMG'cy BATT'ry POWER TO U.W.T. & LT. | | ✓ |
| CABIN BAROMETER SET | ✓ | PROP. MOTORS (DRY, SHORT TIME) | | ✓ |
| CLOCK WOUND AND SET | ✓ | MANIPULATOR, AND CLAW CHECKED | | ✓ |
| CO2 RINGROSE | ✓ | EQUIPMENT FITTED | | |
| CO2 DRAEGER KIT | ✓ | EXTERNAL 6 Glumsbys WEIGHT 60 ks left. for Buoyancy | | |

*With everything ready* Pisces III *waits for the dive with her crew onboard.*

Suddenly, you are told over the radio that you will be fleeted aft. The submersible sets off down the runway; it is very like taking off in a plane really although everything is much slower. She is dragged aft by winches, with restraining wires to prevent her running off the stern, to the end of the ship where the 'A' frame is situated. Stops bring the submersible to an abrupt halt with a thump, and from this position you can see the surface of the sea down beneath you. *Pisces* then settles down into her trolley and remains until the support ship is in exactly the right position for launch.

That night the weather and sea state were reasonable; however, the wind was freshening. Since the charter began, the weather had not been good and in such conditions the best thing to do is to get on with the job and dive as quickly as possible, especially with a crew which suffers from seasickness. Roger was inclined this way and always joked about having a polythene bag ready on the off chance.

It was a standard launch and nothing unusual happened. Once in the water and disconnected from our towline, we were given the signal by radio from the Controller "Clear to vent". So although it was 1.30 am and the ship still had a sleepy atmosphere when we left it, we were very much awake as we headed towards the seabed at least 1,500 feet below.

It is always an advantage for one of the crew to have been down on the preceding dive, specially on deep dives, when it might take at least half an hour to reach the bottom. One may not necessarily be dropped very near to the job in hand but it is certainly reassuring to know what to expect. Surface and subsurface currents are sometimes very unpredictable, more so after a period of bad weather, and they may carry the submersible some way from the work site before she reaches the bottom.

As we approached I told Roger what to expect on the bottom, and as I was fairly new to cable burial, I was looking forward to improving my technique and gaining more experience. It was clear that the task of burying this cable would involve both of us working pretty extensively as it required a great deal of concentration.

It took us about 20 minutes to reach the bottom, when *Pisces* settled out in flat terrain on soft sand. The visibility was extremely good at that depth and we could see six to eight feet with our lights; there were a good many fish about, mainly members of the cod family, such as snaith, but also an occasional eel. The trim was very nearly perfect so we were able to move off without much delay, having first passed to the surface by underwater telephone a report on bottom conditions. Sometimes our communications were interrupted by dolphins, as though their squeaks were a crossed line on the telephone, however we never saw them.

The pilot needs full concentration when moving towards the pinger which marks where burying work must start; he must use the directional headset to get a good pinger bearing, and at the same time must keep to economic speed. The observer meantime is often a little  frustrated and feels that events are taking longer than they should; all he can do is to peer out of his port into the gloom, letting the pilot know if he is running into anything and generally keeping the life support systems going to maintain a reasonable atmosphere inside the submersible.

That night—actually it was then early morning—we did not take very long to reach the cable, in fact we came across it before we reached the pinger. This is quite common, because unless you are dropped at right angles to the cable one often meets it at a slant angle as you travel towards the pinger; then it becomes a question of which way to turn to start the job.

Suddenly to come across a man-made object deep down in the ocean in a completely alien environment gives one quite a jolt each time. Sadly, nowadays, the oceans are becoming polluted, especially offshore. In the North Sea, for instance, the seabed is literally littered with man-made debris, from beer cans to pipe laying equipment. However an area such as the North Atlantic was completely unspoilt, apart from a very occasional isolated object.

It was Roger's first dive on this charter, while it was my second, and it always takes a little time to get used to the conditions on a new site. So for the first hour Roger settled down operating the mud pump, manipulating the nozzle into the correct position as he moved along and generally getting a feel of *Pisces* for the job in hand. We stopped around 4 o'clock, had a cup of coffee and sorted out the plan of the dive. Next I took over for my first spell. Cable burial varies in different parts of the ocean because of the nature of the bottom; as we were travelling west down a gentle slope the bottom became softer and consequently the cable began to go down into a trench more easily. This section of the Post Office cable was armoured and therefore fairly heavy; it was a good sight to see it falling into the trench made by the blast of the water jets from the nozzle with the mud liquefying on top of it. It had been expected that we would have to do three or four passes to get this cable down into a deep enough trough. As time went on both of us began to get a little better at directing the jet on exactly the right part of the cable and as the bottom conditions were very flat with no obstacles in the way and the mud was nice and soft, and we found conditions excellent. Thus the work was enjoyable as the dawn would be breaking 1,650 feet above us.

While you are working and concentrating hard, with your left hand driving the submersible by operating the two motors while your right guides the nozzle onto the cable you never feel tired; yet as soon as you stop and hand over to the observer,

*The Post Office cable deep in the Atlantic after one pass by* Pisces III.

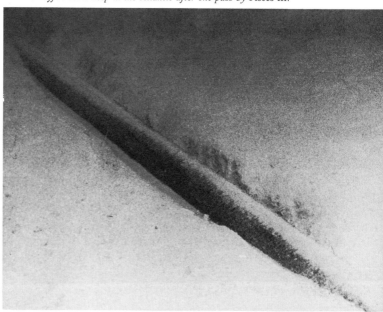

*After a second pass with the mud nozzle the cable is well in trench and mud is beginning to settle on it.*

then sit back in the corner of the submersible and relax, you look at your watch and realise that the support ship is just waking up for breakfast; then maybe you feel a little weary. Our purpose on this run was to go as far west as possible on one single pass, having buried the previous section to a depth of 12 inches with three passes.

Just before we were due to surface as our battery volts were getting low Roger was pumping away; he noticed up ahead of him that the heavy armoured cable was just lifting off the bottom. We stopped—it must have been around 6.30 in the morning—had another cup of coffee and Roger finished off his last tasty sandwich to discuss this little problem, which was all too familiar to both of us.

The cable ahead of us was being held up by an uneven bottom or maybe an obstacle on the seabed which had not been picked up by the surveyors who laid the cable. By then the depth was a little over 1,700 feet and our battery volts were

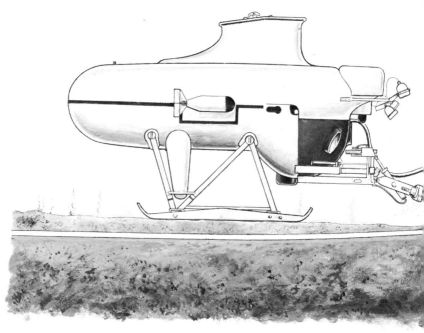

*A trench on the ocean bed left the cable suspended, where it might easily snag a fishing trawl.*

low; but it was well worth investigating this problem ahead so as to give the next pilots an indication of what they might expect.

The coffee was put away and we moved off slowly to investigate. Sure enough, after travelling only a few more feet, we came across the reason why the cable was off the seabed. There was a trench in the seabed ahead and the cable crossed it in front of us. As we moved forward along the cable, it gradually rose higher and higher, so we knew then that this would entail a lot of work in blasting away both sides of this trough to allow the cable to settle itself once again on the seabed. However clever you are at burying the rest of the cable, sure enough the trawler who might snag it would certainly find this one length which was conveniently suspended for him if it was left uncovered.

The extent of the trough was some 20 to 25 feet so we moved backwards and forwards taking video recordings of the cable,

passing information to the surface via the underwater telephone and informing them that we were going to start cutting
away with our manipulator nozzle at the eastern bank before
requesting to surface.

It was just before 8 o'clock when we had completed a couple
of passes at this bank. We knew that most of the crew in the
support ship would have been informed that we were about to
start the surfacing procedure so we took some last video
recordings of the section completed, deployed the pinger,
which we had carried with us, and then moved away from the
cable. This last part of the dive since finding the suspended
cable had perhaps taken only 45 minutes, but it made all the
difference to our mental state as most of the previous few hours
had been straightforward cable burial work and we had
quickly fallen into that routine. 'This will add some days to the
job.' I commented to Roger.

It takes a time for all preparations to be made on the surface, but soon we heard on our underwater telephone the sound of the Gemini's outboard approaching our buoy, even though it was 1,700 feet above us, and this meant that very soon we would be given permission to surface. Roger began pumping oil into our ballast bags to get positively buoyant as this was the method used for ascending from anything below 250 feet. High pressure air is very valuable and the external pressure on our ballast tanks would be such at this depth, that it would use a lot of it to give positive buoyancy by just using these tanks; so a submersible is designed to surface by becoming light on oil as well as on air.

Permission to ascend was at last granted and as we pumped more oil to the ballast bags we gently lifted off and started the steady rise to the surface. We had no indication of weather and assumed conditions to be very much as we had left them, a little choppy but nothing to worry about. Everything was stowed away; we finished a few scraps of food, except for the odd half sandwich that was left. When we approached the surface we noticed the light changing; although we knew the time we had not mentally adjusted to the fact that it was daylight and a new day was just beginning.

At 9.18 am we reached the surface and it seemed that the sun was shining because it was very light and one could see the reflection of the rays of the sun; however when *Pisces* is on the surface the ports are below the water, so one cannot see direct sunlight. Breakfast, a real breakfast, was only about half an hour away, but we were entirely in the hands of the support ship so I could only relax and think of eggs and bacon.

'Welcome back', came the voice of Ralph Henderson, our Surface Officer, over the VHF radio; he gave Roger instructions to manoeuvre his submersible so that lines could be attached as the support ship approached us. It takes a little concentration, even then, for the pilot who must listen very carefully to the orders coming over the VHF radio to make quite sure he does not operate his motors when divers are in the water; yet he must operate them at once when ordered because the recovery routine is very precise and must be carried out correctly.

*We heard the diver clambering onboard.*

We heard the Gemini approaching again, this time carrying the tow rope; next we heard the diver clambering down the back of the submersible then jump into the water; so our towline at this time had been connected. Sure enough, the voice of the Gemini driver came across loud and clear telling

57

the Surface Officer on his VHF radio 'Towline connected'. Then once again we heard the diver clambering onboard.

Suddenly the water alarm started to chatter. We were both instantly aware of this signal, but subconsciously we each assumed that there was some condensation which was causing the very sensitive instrument in the aft sphere to activate. However a second or two later we heard over the VHF a distinctly alarming voice almost shouting 'The diver is indicating something'.

Almost at the same time our stern took a very sharp dip backwards. This was totally unexpected and very alarming; then I saw to my horror that the depth gauge needle was racing back past the 100 foot mark. We had no idea what had happened, but obviously the submersible had suddenly become extremely heavy by the stern. We were going backwards toward the deep, and fast too.

# 5. Sunk to the Bottom of the Sea

The next few minutes were hectic. At 175 feet there was a sudden jolt and then we began to heave around violently. One second the submersible was level, the next it was standing on its tail or looking towards the seabed. The braided nylon tow rope was somehow holding us suspended beneath the support ship, although never designed to take such strain.

'What the hell is going on', I almost shouted to Roger, but already knew what it was. The aft sphere was somehow completely flooded with sea water, so the submersible was over a ton heavier than she should be in water; any second the tow line would part.

Seconds dragged into minutes and we were still suspended. The terrible motion continued, and with it loose equipment was hurled around inside the sphere.

We switched on the underwater telephone and almost unbelievably we heard a distorted voice say 'Hang on, we'll send a diver down with another rope for you'. The voice could not know that it would have been almost suicide for a diver to attempt this, but the mere fact of hearing an outside voice had the effect of bringing us to our senses.

'Must release the drop weight', said Roger, and somehow he found the releasing handle which was clipped behind his seat. This was by no means an easy task, even at the best of times, but it would make us 400 lbs lighter, and was some positive action on our part while every effort was being made on the surface.

The noises coming over the underwater telephone were loud—the surface waves crashing against the support ship,

*The drop weight release penetrator with its spanner. Somehow Roger Mallinson managed to operate the release while Pisces III was dangling beneath Voyager before the towline parted.*

its own propeller noise, our motion, and on top of all that, a voice still encouraging us to hang on. Roger made a final turn and the drop weight was released, whilst I tried to communicate on the underwater telephone. Only two or three minutes had passed since the aft sphere had flooded, but it already seemed an age. Both of us wished the terrible bucking motion to cease, but we knew that if it did, then our last physical link with the surface would be broken.

Suddenly there was an audible crack and the motion ceased. The towline had parted.

The submersible at once adopted a 90° stern down attitude and began to sink very rapidly towards the seabed. It became dark as the depth gauge began to race past the 250 foot mark. This really did galvanize us into action. The large sonar set was hanging by its electrical cable out of its bracket and was an obvious danger; we disconnected it and threw it at our feet, which were then standing on the penetrators at the back of the sphere. Automatically, Roger reached for the underwater telephone and began to call out the depth to the surface. '300 feet, 350 feet . . . 400 feet'. Apart from the depth gauge racing round, we could not sense how fast we were travelling towards the seabed.

'This is it then', I said to Roger, as my brain began to work again but I did not really know what I meant. Automatically we started to go through emergency procedures, although this sort of accident had never been envisaged. Electrical power —120, 24 and 12 volt systems—were each switched off to prevent fire on impact. Rapidly, we placed seat covers, cushions, and anything else that was soft at the back of the sphere behind us. Then we waited.

'800 feet, 900 feet, 1000 feet . . .' We could see the luminous depth gauge above us, like a clock gone mad, still registering our descent. During the ascent had we drifted to the west into much deeper water? Would the submersible withstand the impact? These and other thoughts were racing through my mind at hectic speed.

'1200 feet, 1300 feet . . . 1400 feet'.

'Must get there soon' I said to Roger.

'Bite on a rag before we hit the bottom' he replied; but I never made it.

At 1575 feet exactly the submersible hit the seabed stern first. There was severe jolt, the depth gauge pointer came to an abrupt halt. Then complete quiet.

For a second neither of us dared to move. Would we tip over backwards or lurch forwards? It was still pitch black inside the sphere. Even in the dark I instinctively scribbled in my note book the words 'on Bottom' but guessed at the time as my watch was not luminous.

In the dark the author recorded in his notebook that Pisces III *was on the bottom; but his time was incorrect.*

Slowly and carefully we shifted from our cramped position. Deliberately, Roger reached up for the main 120 volt breaker. If nothing happened when he made the switch then our main battery would be damaged and the position more critical than ever.

'Click' went the switch in the darkness and immediately the

small dome lights came on. With relief we relaxed for a second. Electrical power was still available.

Almost immediately we were brought back harshly to our senses by a loud hissing noise inside the sphere. 'What's that?'. But we knew almost immediately that the main oxygen bottle was leaking. Our vital oxygen supply, so precious for life support, was indiscriminately revitalising the atmosphere.

With the submersible's attitude tilted 90° backwards, and the inside of the sphere almost spherical, we were completely disorientated. Where a piece of equipment had previously been at your elbow for convenience, it was now hanging somewhere above your head. There was a shambles everywhere inside the sphere. Experience again played a vital part as Roger dived under the cushions to his left and groped for the main oxygen bottle, found the right end and turned off the bottle. The hissing stopped.

There was no time then to worry about how much we had wasted. There began an immediate detailed search for all our life support equipment. Nothing else mattered, as we had electrical power, and the sphere had remained watertight on impact. Yet it was obvious that we must expect to be down on the seabed for a long time, although it was not mentioned by either of us at this stage.

Emergency power was our next concern. Somewhere amongst the shambles was a small dry cell 12-volt battery, wired into the communication system and able to give power to the under-water telephone if main batteries failed; it could even run the scrubber for a short time as a last resort. The battery was found and, although on its side and dangling by its wires, appeared to be undamaged.

Because of our attitude the scrubber, complete with canister, was lying horizontally but was still secured to its bracket. Here was another cliff hanger. If this vital piece of equipment did not work, if it was damaged beyond repair, then our survival time would be short indeed. Gingerly I placed the scrubber motor upright, re-secured the canister and nodded to Roger. 'Try it'. Click went the switch, and to my amazement, the motor purred into life.

It had only been a few minutes since the submersible had struck the bottom, but suddenly I felt very tired. We had been up most of the previous day and night, and just a short while ago had been so near to a bath, breakfast and welcome rest. Then this. It was still almost impossible to understand our predicament, but my body gave the game away. I was shaking like a leaf and very hot.

Next thing was to try communications with the surface. I did not expect much result, but anything was better than nothing. The communications breakers were above my head and as I made the switch an anxious voice, loud and clear with little interference, came from the control box. '*Pisces, Pisces*, this is *Voyager* . . . Do you read, over'

We selected the down transducer which at our attitude was more up than down, then replied 'This is *Pisces*, Yes, we read you loud and clear. Go ahead.'

'Ah, hear you loud and clear *Pisces*. What is your position down there'. The voice had changed since we had answered, so obviously they had been trying to contact us ever since the tow line parted; it was loud, confident and gave us both a good deal of encouragement when it was so much needed. There was no time for a long description of the situation of the seabed, so I replied that we would get ourselves sorted out and call back in ten minutes or so.

It was obvious to both of us that we must organise ourselves as quickly as possible, then settle down to conserve our vital power supply and life support. By standing up, searching for equipment and talking, we were using up far too much oxygen. Luckily the benches, which normally run fore and aft for the pilot observer to lie down and view out of the ports, had come adrift on impact. It was, therefore, relatively easy to re-arrange them on either side of the sphere; but care had to be taken as they were resting on the penetrators at one end and hydraulic valves at the other. The intention was that when we

| Time | | | | | |
|------|---|---|---|---|---|
| 1247 | $O^2$ 1 BOTTLE 3400 OTHER BOTTLE 26 | | | | |
| | ATTITUDE 90° STERN DOWN | | | | |
| | Psi 2 (#1) 3300 ↑ Si WILL CALL | | | | |

were lying down in pitch darkness, everything would be to hand.

Many minor modifications were made to the set-up over the next three and a half days, but within 10 minutes we had basically re-arranged the inside of the submersible to the new attitude. The underwater telephone microphone had enough lead to hang down in front of us and the control box was within reach. The main oxygen supply was buried under Roger's bench, so we reverted to the reserve supply bottle which was three inches from my head; I was able to monitor our consumption from this bottle accurately during the first 24-hour period, as the contents gauge was staring me full in the face. The one item which could not be controlled from the lying down position was the scrubber switch on the pilot's console; this was above our feet on the other side of the sphere. To keep the $CO_2$ at an acceptable level, the scrubber had to be run for at least ten minutes in every $\frac{3}{4}$ hour, although occasionally neither of us woke up to operate the switch, as the account of the next few days will show.

Once organised and lying down again, we contacted the support ship and gave a more detailed report. Their main concern was our state of health and our life support supply remaining. We had not been injured on impact; and the submersible and its systems were still functioning correctly, even at 90° to the horizontal; so our report contained detailed figures of oxygen supply remaining and the state of $CO_2$ canisters.

These life support figures which we passed were subsequently radioed back to Barrow-in Furness; there the latest time for the rescue operation to be complete was calculated and the table on the following page shows how it worked out.

These calculations turned out to be very accurate, although one important factor was not known at that time. As the main

*The underwater communications log onboard* Voyager *records a detailed report telephoned from* Pisces III *on the seabed.*

| L$^{TH}$ | CANS | SCRUBBER | WORKS | BATTERY VOLTS 110 |
| TANKS POSSIBLY FLOODED | | | AIR BOTTLES 2 X2000 |
| $\frac{1}{2}$ HOUR . | MORALE | FANTASTIC . |

Table of Life Support Systems on PIII Striking Bottom

1. OXYGEN ($O_2$)
   $O_2$ available on first diving:
   1 cylinder @ 3000 $= \dfrac{3000}{147} \times \dfrac{20}{624}$ cubic feet
   1 cylinder @ 2400 $= \dfrac{2400}{147} \times \dfrac{20}{624}$ cubic feet
   Total $= \dfrac{5400}{147} \times \dfrac{20}{624}$ $= 118$ cubic fee
   or 3340 litres

   Dive duration up to incident $= 8$ hours.

   *Assume usage of 1 litre/min/man during dive.*

   Then $O_2$ used $= 16 \times 60$ $= 960$ litres
   Available $O_2$ left $= 3340 - 960$ $= 2380$ litres
   If usage reduced to 0.25 litres/min/man, then
   available duration $= \dfrac{2380}{0.5} = 4760$ minutes $= 79.5$ *hours*

   Assume
   (a) *Cylinder pressures were as given above prior to dive.*
   (b) *$O_2$ was used @ 1 litre/minute/men during first dive.*
   (c) *$O_2$ to be used @ $\frac{1}{4}$ litre/minute/man after incident.*

**Therefore latest time for rescue complete** $= 16.00$ *hrs*
$Saturday$

2. CARBON DIOXIDE ($CO_2$)
$CO_2$ Scrubbing Capability. LIOH at start of dive
$= 2$ full cans plus one with 18 hours use
LIOH used during dive $= 16$ hours. ie total usage on 1 can
$= 34$ hours.
**Therefore total scrubbing capability left** $= 134$ **hours.**

3. POWER REQUIREMENTS FOR SCRUBBERS.
Load factor $= 25\%$ Current requirement $= 2$ amps.
Therefore average current required $= \frac{1}{2}$ amp.
**Thus requirement before $O_2$ is exhausted** $= 79.5 \times \frac{1}{2}$
$= 40$ ampere ho

66

oxygen bottle was buried, we passed its contents as 2400 litres, which was the reading taken 15 minutes before on the surface. In fact when two days later the reserve bottle was exhausted, the main bottle content was found to have only 1900 litres; so actually we had used 16 man-hours of oxygen on the way to the seabed.

Food was not really important, and we had practically none, but there was ample to drink. For the next two hours we made quite sure that everything was as conveniently placed as possible and began to settle into a routine. Although the temperature inside the sphere at approximately 50°F was not cold, the humidity at 95% was high, so it felt colder than it was. My sweater was 1575 feet above in the support ship, so I put on a life jacket underneath my overalls, and also wrapped rags round my chest to keep warm. Roger had been sensible enough to bring his thick red sweater with him.

The shaking in our bodies died down, and in pitch darkness we relaxed and discussed the situation. Vickers Oceanics and its personnel were known to us, and also the whereabouts of our other submersibles. We began to visualise what steps would be taken for a rescue, but we never guessed what huge preparations and dynamic efforts were already being made just one hour after the accident.

The towline parted at 09.22 on Wednesday morning. By 10.00 a.m. the *Voyager* had contacted Vickers Oceanics at Barrow with the message, '*Pisces III* aft sphere flooded, and the submersible bottomed in 1575 feet, 50° 09′.15N, 11° 07′.7W, about 150 miles SW of Cork'.

From that moment on a stupendous organisation swung into action in Barrow, Cork and at sea.

The basic situation of submersibles suitable for rescuing *Pisces III* at such a depth was very quickly established as follows:–

*Pisces II* was on board *Vickers Venturer* operating in the North Sea, and 150 miles from the nearest port of Aberdeen.

*Pisces IV* and *Pisces V* were operating on east and west coasts of Canada respectively.

*Pisces I* was refitting at Base and was not available.

Therefore the closest was *Pisces II*; contact was immediately made with her in the North Sea, and she was ordered to the nearest port. At the same time, the Royal Naval Submarine Base at Helensburgh in Scotland had been informed and instituted SUBSMASH, the code word used for any submarine accident; also the International Hydrodynamics Ltd (HYCO) in Canada, owners of *Pisces IV* and *V*, had been asked for assistance.

My wife, who worked for Vickers in the Research and Development Team as secretary to the manager, learnt of the accident shortly after 10.00 a.m. from Peter Messervy, General Manager of Vickers Oceanics, so straight away she set off to Oceanics, only half a mile away across the water in Barrow, to find out the full story. In her own words, she was immediately impressed and given great confidence by the vigorous activity taking place in Oceanics, with Peter Messervy quickly on the telephone to the world. His intimate knowledge of the international submarine business and the personalities involved gave him immediate access to every available rescue system in Great Britain, the United States and Canada.

By noon events ashore had moved fast. Back on the seabed, we were feeling more relaxed. In pitch darkness, although communications were sometimes poor, we spoke every 30 minutes or so with the support ship, but to conserve oxygen our own conversation was reduced to necessities.

It was 12 hours since *Pisces III* had left the surface at the start of the dive and our biggest concern at this time was the submersible itself. When not talking, both of us were running through in our minds the various systems that were required for life support. On more than one occasion, we both spoke at once about one item of equipment or another that needed testing. The pressure hull appeared intact, but the humidity was already high. Every few minutes a drop of water would fall onto my face as the condensation ran down the side of the sphere. On went the torch, and a quick check of the penetrators showed that all were intact and not leaking. It was disturbing at first, these drops of water, always tested by taste to see if they were salt; but during the next three days, the condensation provided refreshment to the mouth and face.

The two main battery boxes, containing 120 volt, 12 volt and 24 volt batteries, were on their sides. At that time the voltage of all three systems were checked almost continuously to see if we were losing power. The acid could be running to

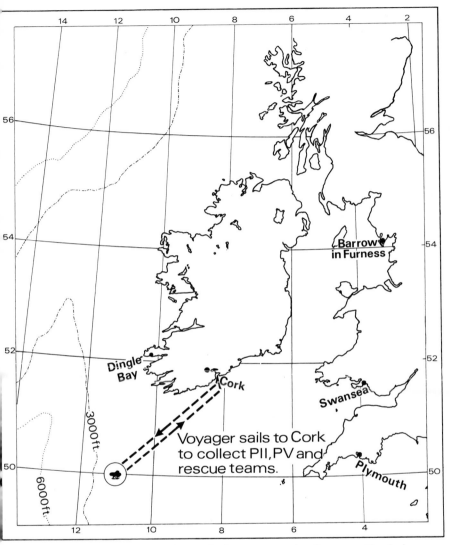

Voyager sails to Cork to collect PII, PV and rescue teams.

Pisces III *sank about 150 miles from Cork, the nearest port where* Voyager *could embark rescue craft. She lay 1,575 feet deep but the sea bottom quickly dropped to far greater depths nearby.*

the bottom of the boxes and therefore there was a possibility of an acid leak or drop in electric power; then the battery boxes themselves may have been damaged on impact. We could probably have done nothing about it if voltage had began to drop; however everything looked OK during these initial few hours.

At 12.47 we again passed by underwater telephone a report on the state of our life support equipment. Already however, we were aware that it was taking longer than it should to reduce the $CO_2$ level to an acceptable figure 0.5% when running the scrubber. This was because the $CO_2$ canister had been used for the previous dive of 9 hours, so the pellets in the can were becoming saturated with condensation and so were less effective. This was worrying. There were two spare canisters available but it would not have been wise to use a new one too soon, as it would then be exposed to the same high humidity. All that could be done was to shake the old canister whilst running the scrubber and hope that it would continue to re-remove $CO_2$ from the atmosphere. We allowed the $CO_2$ level to rise a little in consequence and the effects of this were to become more apparent during the next few days.

# 6. The Long Wait

Another problem was facing us on the seabed. The urine bottle was full; it was of a small plastic type, which originally contained half a gallon of domestic detergent. We sat for a while contemplating. Although humorous to recall, it required careful thought as the top was also missing amongst the debris at the bottom of the sphere, and would have required too much expenditure of energy to find it. Eventually a solution—we emptied the contents of the bottle into a strong plastic bag, two of which were carried in the submersible for rubbish, and continued to use the bottle. The bag was secured and carefully placed under the benches. As can be imagined, this little process made the atmosphere rather unpleasant, but it did not take us too long to get used to it.

At 3 pm on Wednesday afternoon, the day of the accident, detailed planning was going ahead back at Barrow. The log kept there, the centre of the rescue operation, records the help and assistance offered from all quarters. The first objective of the rescue team, led by Peter Messervy, was to relieve *Voyager* as soon as possible at the scene of the accident, so that she could return to Cork in Southern Ireland, where she could pick up the submersibles, rescue equipment and experts needed. It was 150 sea miles to Cork and for *Voyager* to get alongside and start loading it meant a $13\frac{1}{2}$ hour dash at full speed. So from the moment she left the accident spot till the time she arrived back ready to start rescue operations, 27 hours would pass—plus loading time in Cork.

Our position was marked by two buoys on the surface, but to keep the underwater telephone communication contact alive

Len Edwards, the captain of *Voyager*, needed to exercise constant skill and seamanship as the wind was freshening from the west to make things difficult. Contact had to be maintained at all costs so as to pinpoint the position of *Pisces III* on the seabed for the rescue submersibles when the time came; thus a relief ship was required to remain in touch with *Pisces III* through the portable underwater telephone equipment while *Voyager* returned to Cork.

Throughout the morning and well into Wednesday afternoon, the search continued for the relief ship. At the same time detailed plans were made to fly submersibles into Cork: in addition all Vickers' light aircraft were recalled to Barrow so that they could fly people and stores as required. The Ministry of Defence (Navy) advised Vickers that *Voyager* should send a 'Mayday' distress signal to attract the nearest vessel of any type, while the Royal Navy searched the fleet for the nearest ship available.

As far as the Royal Navy was concerned, *HMS Valiant*, a nuclear submarine, and *HMS Andrew*, a conventional submarine, could possibly reach the area before midnight, so both were ordered to the spot by radio. The research vessel, *HMS Hecate*, which was later to play a vital role in rescue operations, could arrive early on Thursday morning; she was ordered to load special ropes and then head straight for the scene of the accident.

Both the US Navy and the Irish Navy were making similar efforts to supply ships. The US salvage ship *Aeolus* was 10 hours away at 2 pm on Wednesday afternoon, and proceeded at full speed, while an Irish Naval vessel in Dingle Bay made preparations to sail.

Yet by the middle of the afternoon, *Voyager* was still unable to leave for Cork as no ship had arrived to guard our position. Completely unknown to us on the seabed an RAF Nimrod, a highly sophisticated anti-submarine aircraft, was at that time flying above *Voyager*; it dropped sonar buoys and attempted to contact *Pisces III* on the seabed through them. However we never heard the Nimrod's messages, so it was unable to accept the responsibility of maintaining contact with us if *Voyager* departed. *Voyager* was therefore given firm instructions to remain on station until relieved by another ship.

We were not given any bad news on the seabed and during the afternoon began to settle into a routine. By 4 pm it was cold and damp but communications were good. Further instructions were passed from *Voyager* to remain quiet and still; if cold we were advised to unzip the seat covers and climb in as a sleeping bag. This was no good as the covers had recently been changed and were not the sort that unzip; however, this suggestion made us think. We had been lying for the past few hours on either side of the sphere and shivering a little against the cold damp sides; by simply pushing the benches together and rearranging things a little we could provide each other with warmth and at the same time we could share the rubber cover used for the video equipment; we also found some rags to help keep us warm. After that we immediately began to feel less cold.

At 5 pm there came from *Voyager* a simple instruction to us. 'Keep listening constantly on the underwater telephone. We are about to test another transducer'. Nothing more was said but we felt that at least something must be happening on the surface. The underwater telephone loudspeaker was switched on, and we lay back in the darkness awaiting events. Very little happened for 45 minutes. All we could hear, loud and clear, was the pinger which we had left at the end of our run on the cable. It sounded very close 'Ping, Ping, Ping' . . . every $1\frac{1}{2}$ seconds a relentless sharp noise which very quickly caused increasing headaches, but we had to keep the volume high to hear *Voyager*'s new transducer. 'Ping, Ping, Ping' . . . No word from *Voyager*.

Just as we were wondering what the problem might be, *Voyager*, loud and clear, came in with new instructions.

'Ralph Henderson and David Mayo will shortly be transferring to another ship *Sir Tristram*. There will be a break in communications. Maintain constant listening watch on the underwater telephone. We will be in touch again soon.'

So the efforts to get relief for *Voyager* had finally paid off. The Royal Fleet Auxiliary Vessel, *Sir Tristram*, had answered *Voyager*'s call and arrived on the scene at 6.15 on Wednesday evening. Actually the BP tanker *British Kiwi* had altered her course to our rescue even sooner, but *Sir Tristram* got there first.

We acknowledged these instructions and listened to the underwater telephone. It was easy to imagine what was happening on the surface but of course we had no idea of the weather, or that the wind was still increasing from the west.

No more messages were heard, but 20 minutes later there was a distant and loud thrashing noise over the loudspeaker; our mother ship, *Voyager*, was making off over the horizon at full speed to Cork. In a way this was a significant moment for us; our trusted support ship was leaving us, but having served in the Royal Navy for nine years, I knew it would be a long time before the friendly noise of *Voyager's* propellers would be heard again. However, this was not discussed between us on the seabed.

Once *Voyager* had departed, it was time to make a few refinements to the inside of the sphere. Several important items of equipment which needed checking constantly were still out of reach and the small hand-held torches were being used too often. The barometer, which indicated the pressure inside the sphere, was unscrewed and tied close to hand. The pressure was then $28\frac{1}{2}$ inches, which is approximately 2 inches below atmospheric pressure, but this was quite safe. Every time the scrubber was run, the pressure fell as poisonous $CO_2$ was removed from the atmosphere, however the lithium hydroxide canister was taking even longer to remove the $CO_2$ and it needed changing badly. We still delayed this until absolutely necessary.

To maintain the pressure, oxygen from the reserve bottle was leaked into the sphere. As the bottle was next to my head, I tied the barometer nearby and was able to keep a careful eye on our consumption of oxygen. It appeared that we were still using too much, so we were determined to reduce this through the night whilst waiting for *Voyager* to return and it should have required no real effort to keep quiet and still as we were both very tired.

For two hours nothing was heard from the surface, but the pinger pinged away, its monotonous noise keeping us awake. At last it was 8.30 pm, two and a half hours after *Voyager* had departed—communication with the surface was once again re-established.

'Sorry about the delay, we have been having communication

troubles. How are you down there?' David Mayo's friendly voice once again came over the loudspeaker from our new support ship *Sir Tristram*. We passed a short situation report and settled back into the darkness; our task was to stay alive, while the task of the rescuers seemed ten times more demanding.

As the news arrived in Barrow that Sir Tristram was on the way to relieve *Voyager*, plans were in full swing to fly rescue submersibles to Cork to meet her. *Vickers Venturer* (with *Pisces II* aboard) had called in by radio telephone from the North Sea to say that she had arranged to transfer *Pisces II* to a rig supply ship in the North Sea which could steam four knots faster than *Venturer*; once the transfer had taken place the supply ship would proceed straight into Teesport. As it worked out, the supply vessel came alongside *Venturer* almost without stopping, swung over a crane normally used for laying pipe, and picked *Pisces II* off the deck of *Venturer*; meanwhile four team members, including Bob Eastaugh, the operations manager and most experienced operations man in Oceanics, all scrambled aboard and the supply ship streaked off towards Teesport. *Venturer* continued to Hartlepool for fuel and stores, then

Vickers Venturer *with* Pisces II *were operating in the North Sea 150 miles from Aberdeen when* Pisces III *sank. Here they are seen on another occasion operating off Scotland.*

turned south in the North Sea and headed off for the long voyage to the rescue area; against worsening weather and heavy seas, she battled into the English Channel and towards Land's End.

At about the time we had re-established communications with *Sir Tristram* after the departure of *Voyager*, *Pisces II* was arriving in Teesport.

There was good news too from the other side of the Atlantic. A 'phone call from Canada received in Barrow said that *Pisces V* was being loaded in Halifax, Nova Scotia and would be ready to take off at 5.30 pm; this meant she might arrive in Cork about 1 am on Thursday. *Pisces V*, sister submersible of *Pisces II* and *Pisces III*, could dive to a depth of 6,000 feet and her assistance would be invaluable.

Two other important events were recorded in the Base log at Barrow on that Wednesday afternoon; briefly recorded, they were to prove vital during the rescue.

15.07   US Navy rang. *CURV* confirmed (Controlled underwater recovery vehicle)

17.25   US Navy 'phoned regarding *John Cabot* which is at Swansea.

Peter Messervy, assisted not only by the experts in Vickers and the United Kingdom but also from across the Atlantic, made his plans and left for Cork at 8.20 pm on Wednesday evening. Control of the rescue operation shifted with him, and with the initial planning complete hopes were high for an early recovery.

At 10 pm back in *Pisces III*, the first $CO_2$ canister was clearly doing no good, as the scrubber had been running for a full 20 minutes without decreasing the level of $CO_2$ in the atmosphere. Normally the new $CO_2$ canister is prepared onboard the support ship, as it is an awkward task; the top and bottom of the canister have to be removed with a large screwdriver, and as the seal is very good, a certain amount of energy is needed. Under normal conditions this would be no problem, but that night it took me three times as long to prepare the canister. By the time it was ready I could feel the effects of the lack of oxygen and a high $CO_2$ content in the atmosphere. Unavoidably also, a certain amount of lithium hydroxide dust gets in to the atmosphere when changing a can and this irritates the throat. However, when the task was completed, we celebrated by sharing half a cup of cold coffee and a glucose biscuit from the emergency ration pack. It was hardly a banquet and not quite as good as a breath of Lake District air, but at least we both felt a great deal better. The scrubber was run for a good period to reduce the $CO_2$ below $.5\%$.

About this time, I felt that Roger had something on his mind and eventually he came out with it.

'I'm sorry Roger,' he said 'but I will have to. I cannot wait any longer.'

Many people have asked us since the accident how we managed to relieve ourselves whilst on the seabed. This was mainly out of well meant and humorous curiosity, but I believe it is significant to relate the facts. We had become very sensitive to our atmosphere control, as this was our only task apart from communicating with the surface. Roger had obviously been lying in the darkness for some time in discomfort, but did not want to upset the routine inside the sphere and cause an unpleasant smell. We had always joked in the operations team that Roger only 'went' once in a sea voyage and maybe this was on his mind as well.

Once again then, this problem was thought out and a simple solution found. The new $CO_2$ canister had been covered by another strong plastic bag and Roger used this, which was adequate; then we emptied the First Aid Box, and put the plastic bag in that. Next the box was secured, and being airtight, was placed at the bottom of the sphere. After the operation the scrubber was run and that was that. Roger felt a lot better and I could see him grinning in the darkness, although somewhat out of breath.

Communications with *Sir Tristram* were bad that night and several times there were long periods when we heard nothing at all. However, at 1.30 am on Thursday evening we received one message from David Mayo which we misinterpreted, but all the same it gave us a great boost, as our spirits were beginning to drop a little. The message as we received it was 'Best wishes to *Pisces* crew and hope all goes well, from Queen Elizabeth'. Communications were bad and we assumed wrongly that this message was from Her Majesty the Queen, but on the seabed we could hardly know that *Queen Elizabeth II*, the great Cunard cruise liner, had passed by earlier in the day and had offered assistance. She had then gone on her way and relayed the welcome message, which certainly had a great effect on us and gave tremendous encouragement when communications were bad.

Through the night, messages got through between us and *Sir Tristram* from time to time. The two domestic timers were set every half-hour, one to go off in 30 minutes and the other in two hours just in case we slept through the first. The inside of the sphere was wringing wet with condensation and it felt really rather cold again; each of us was concerned that we might fall asleep and allow the $CO_2$ to build up to a dangerous level, so both woke up as the 30 minute timer went off. On several occasions I woke but was not at first fully aware what had happened, and in the pitch dark it took a few moments to get thinking again. I found those few important moments were the worst, as I lay and forced my mind to think straight after the timer had gone off: it was all too easy to drift back to sleep again, forgetting to check the level of $CO_2$, run the scrubber for a time, and reset the timer; indeed this did happen more than once.

Only some 18 hours after the accident did we get round to thinking about how it had all happened. We had no idea why the aft sphere had suddenly filled with water, and we did not realize that the hatch had completely come away whilst we were on tow. In fact, looking back on that first night, the cause of the accident did not seem to have any significance to us, there was just the realisation that the sphere was flooded, and our thoughts were on how the rescuers were going to pick us up.

In situations like ours individual personalities become more clearly defined. Roger's mind was very active and I could almost hear him thinking; every few moments he would say something like 'I think it is best if we are picked up by a rope around the frame at the forward end; here the stresses will be minimised.' However, I was reluctant to get into conversation. First of all, I felt almost relaxed into a sense of waiting and leaving the big decisions to the rescuers. It was still a long time before *Voyager* would return and our consumption of oxygen was still too high. As the hours passed that night Roger ceased to think aloud and conversation became less, probably because of my apparent lack of interest. Apart from the occasional communications check with *Sir Tristram*, very little was said; perhaps my naval discipline helped here, as it was certain that every word spoken and even each thought stirring the mind would use up more oxygen. Our task was to act as vegetables most of the time, but still perform as intelligent human beings every half hour for essential life support jobs.

However the activity ashore was by then in top gear, as rescue submersibles and equipment were beginning to arrive in Cork. Peter Messervy and party flew in at 10.15 pm to find the news that *Pisces V* would probably arrive from Halifax around 2.30 am Thursday morning. As well as the major decisions and consequent arrangements that were being tackled at this time, a host of other problems were facing the rescue team, so Vickers Oceanics base manager, Sandy Hook, was appointed in charge at Cork; he had travelled with Peter Messervy from Barrow and was fully in the picture. Extracts from the base logs kept at Barrow and Cork show that these problems were numerous; for example telephone calls from Al Trice, the field operations manager of HYCO, who owned *Pisces V*, wanted clearance for the pilots of the submersible who were travelling without passports; transport arrangements had to be made, and a tally kept on the exact location of special equipment.

The complexity of the operation was beginning to show. The weather forecasts for the area were still depressing but the rescuers had one distinct advantage; they were all familiar with their business and although this was worldwide, all the equipment, techniques and skills were mutually understood among submersible people. Decisions could be taken quickly, requests for equipment passed by telex, signal or telephone, were immediately clear to all because there was a common technical language, and there was never any hesitation.

At midnight the rig supply vessel *Comet* with *Pisces II* onboard docked in Teesport. On the way in the submersible had been prepared for her air journey and in 25 minutes she was on the road to Teesside Airport, in the safe hands of Bob Eastaugh, the operations manager. Bob was completely dedicated in his job and led the operations team in Vickers Oceanics with tremendous enthusiasm; he was capable of working for days on end without sleep, and the major responsibility of the rescue operations was to fall on his broad shoulders. Like Al Trice, in HYCO, he was sending messages on ahead to Cork in Ireland.

Almost as if the operation had been planned weeks beforehand, *Pisces V* and *Pisces II* arrived in Cork by air within little more than half an hour of each other. At 3.30 am a Royal Canadian Air Force Hercules touched down with *Pisces V* and the HYCO team led by Mike Macdonald, their senior pilot who was well known to Oceanics. Then at 4.12 am the plane carrying *Pisces II* landed and as the dawn was breaking in Cork both submersibles were en route to the dockside ready for the arrival of *Voyager* which was due alongside at 8.15 am on Thursday morning.

# 7. *Voyager* Returns

It had been a long night, cold and damp, and not everything was quite right. Towards morning, between short periods of dozing, we would wake up each time with splitting headaches. Roger was in particular pain, and it was not clear why the pain had increased. The scrubber had been run quite regularly, except when we had slept through the first timer, and the $CO_2$ indicator was not registering an unduly high content in the atmosphere of poisonous gas. What then had altered the situation? One thing was certain, it was taking us a lot longer to work things out and make decisions. While Roger was in a great deal of pain, my headaches were not too bad.

At last we realised what was wrong. Overnight, unknown to us, our attitude had changed slightly; either the benches on which we were lying had slipped down at the head or the submersible had tilted back a little further into the mud. We did not think too much about the cause but once noticed it became obvious that our feet were above our heads when lying down, and this in itself would cause a pain in the head even under normal conditions. What to do? Again a pause for thought. In fact, in pausing, I drifted off to sleep again, to be woken a few minutes later by Roger who was sitting up.

Two solutions were open to us. Either prop up the benches at our head or to turn round and lie the other way. This might not seem a major decision but looking back it took us some time to get sorted out. Propping up the head was not so easy as it sounds as there was little to use, and in the darkness, several attempts were unsuccessful. We therefore tried turning ourselves round end for end.

Switching on the small dome lights, we carefully moved all our equipment to the other side of the sphere. The life support items were our main concern with such vital things as the $CO_2$ contents guage and the domestic timers, which were again re-secured to strategic points close at hand, besides the barometer. Unfortunately, the oxygen bottle was no longer at my feet so it would mean sitting up to operate the valve; but at least we were now closer to the scrubber switch.

This process of changing round took about 30 minutes, and we were exhausted on finishing it. However, once organised, it was certainly far more comfortable, and we settled back into the darkness. This move again showed us that even the smallest movement caused an increase in our breathing rate, and consequently an increase in $CO_2$ being exhaled into the atmosphere. This would in turn cause a longer scrubbing time to remove the $CO_2$ and the need to use more oxygen. We determined not to change round again unless absolutely necessary.

Whilst in *Pisces III* we were intent on doing and thinking as little as possible, in the early hours of Thursday morning, *Voyager* was just an hour's steaming from Cork. At 7.30 am the submersibles and their support equipment were actually on the jetty awaiting her arrival. It had already been a long night for the rescuers, making sure that nothing would be forgotten for the loading that was to follow; submersibles are not complicated machines but they do require support equipment and tools especially designed for each one. *Pisces V*, the Canadian submersible from International Hydrodynamics, would have to be operated from *Voyager* whose basic handling system could easily cope with minor modifications. Yet the electrical charging systems required careful thought before the ship could leave for the open sea again as it would be imperative to charge *Pisces V's* battery immediately after a dive so that she would be ready to go down again. All these problems needed to be sorted out by the experts, but by then more than 80% of Vickers Oceanics operations and base people were either in Cork or on the way.

At 8.15 am on Thursday morning *Voyager* arrived alongside the jetty in Cork Harbour and loading started immediately. *Pisces V* and *Pisces II* were quickly hoisted onboard by large dockside cranes and secured on the two loading trolleys at

Vickers Voyager, *which sailed from Cork with* Pisces V *and* Pisces II *onboard 25 hours after* Pisces III *sank.*

the stern. Just over two hours later everything was secured, and *Voyager* was ready to sail back at high speed to the scene of the accident.

Whilst loading had been going on the press were taking pictures, but also became involved in the loading themselves as Bob Fisher, one of the Oceanics pilots, recalled later. A photographer had been asked to put down his camera and hang on to a steadying rope as a submersible left the ground to be hoisted onboard. The eagerness of the rescuers to get on with their task was infectious.

Peter Messervy said a few words to reporters as he climbed the ladder of *Voyager*. 'If all goes well, we should have *Pisces III* back on the surface in no time. A rescue submersible will go down to locate *Pisces III* carrying with it a lifeline. Once attached, we shall hoist the submersible to the surface. Providing the weather is good, the operation should not take longer than a few hours. This sort of thing has happened before to *Pisces III,* and the rescue was successful within seven hours, the only thing that could defeat us is the weather.'

What Peter Messervy did not mention at that time was that he was one of the crew who were rescued on the previous occasion. The accident to *Pisces III* happened in Vancouver Bay three years before, whilst he was running trials of the submersible after a refit in the International Hydrodynamics yard in North Vancouver. These were early days of submersible operations, and that time there were no alarm systems such as the one later fitted which told us that water was leaking into the aft sphere.

On the trial dive in Vancouver Bay water was leaking very slowly into the aft sphere through a vent hole, normally secured against leaks, and the submersible was becoming heavy by the stern. However, as the leak was only a trickle, it was not until *Pisces III* was operating on the bottom in 600 feet of water that the pilots realised something was amiss. It was then too late to return to the surface in the normal way as *Pisces III* was too heavy to lift herself up.

As luck would have it, another submersible was operating nearby and within two hours was launched to carry out the rescue operation; one and a half hours later a line was attached and winching began.

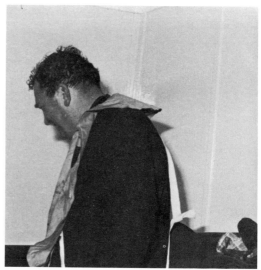

*Peter Messervy was in charge of the rescue operation and had earlier been rescued himself when* Pisces III *stuck on the seabottom at 600 feet.*

Peter Messervy therefore had firsthand knowledge of the problem that was facing him and his team, this time as the rescuers; so he had every confidence all would go well.

Whilst all this was going on in Southern Ireland a change round of support ships was taking place 150 miles out in the rough waters of the Atlantic. *Sir Tristram*, a multi-purpose 6,390 ton fast troop and heavy vehicle carrier, was handing over responsibility, along with David Mayo and Ralph Henderson, to *HMS Hecate*, a 2,898 ton survey ship designed for a combined oceanographical hydrographical role, which had arrived on the scene at 5.45 am that morning.

Our last message from *Sir Tristram* was full of news about things happening in Cork and another warning that there would be a break in communications as a surface transfer took place. The noise of the pinger registered sharply in our ears when the volume control of the underwater telephone loudspeaker was normal, so we had begun to turn it down unless it was time to communicate or special events were about to happen. Thus we turned it up whilst the transfer took place.

This time it was two and a half hours before we heard anything from the surface. At 9.15 am a faint voice was heard above the pinger. *HMS Hecate* was calling us. 'Pisces, Pisces, this is *Hecate*. Do you read, over?' We answered, and like us they just heard the voice. They had been trying for some time to make contact, but the weather had further deteriorated from the west and a gale was blowing. However, the surface did not pass us this information, which could hardly have encouraged us, while if our hearts were made to beat faster that would mean we would breathe harder.

Roger's bad headaches were increasing and when using the torch to check the $CO_2$ level I could see him lying face down holding his head in his hands; however he never mentioned any pain. Apart from this and the damp atmosphere, we were fine and looking forward to hearing news of the *Voyager* and the rescue teams. We did not have long to wait, although time dragged laboriously on the seabed.

At 10.30 am *Voyager* sailed from Cork. Before she left a report came that America's *CURV III* (Remote-Controlled Underwater Recovery Vehicle) was available and already bound from San Diego to Cork; also the *John Cabot*, a Canadian cable ship, had arrived in Cork to await *CURV III's* arrival. To speed the *John Cabot's* departure when the time came, she was moved to a midstream berth from which she could sail at any state of the tide, and a barge was arranged to transfer *CURV* from shore to ship.

'The submersibles are on their way to the area and other systems are standing by when ready', were the messages received by us on the seabed on Thursday morning.

Less than 24 hours after the accident had happened powerful help was on the way. It was to be a British ship carrying Canadian submersibles, operated by pilots from Canada and England, supported by American equipment.

Before I left the Royal Navy my last Captain, Tim Hale, Commanding Officer of the nuclear submarine *HMS Swiftsure*, had commented to me whilst steaming up the Clyde in bad weather a year before. 'You can fix machines if they don't work, sack men if they are idle, but you can do nothing about the bloody weather'.

The weather was doing its best to be bloody that Thursday as *Voyager* steamed towards *HMS Hecate*. It was still blowing from the west, which made for heavy going and cut back her speed.

Yet all was calm on the seabed. At depths below three or four hundred feet you are not aware of bad weather; however, when near the surface, the submersible will be pushed around if there is a heavy swell, and these were the effects we had felt the day before when hanging from the recovery rope before it broke. The support ship, now *HMS Hecate*, was being fully exposed to the rough seas and in the most disturbed water was the underwater telephone transducer; this is a small electronic cylinder-shaped object about the size of a mug, which was hanging over the side of the ship held by an electrical wire and a support rope. So communications deteriorated as the weather worsened.

During the morning several half hour periods passed without anything being heard from the surface. This time it was my turn to expend too much energy in worrying about a problem over which we had little control. As I lay in the darkness, I thought up a simple system for the surface to indicate to us what was happening if all voice communication failed. In fact, I took so much trouble about this, that I found my small notebook and

SIGNALS — ONE GRENADE
EVERY HOUR.
3 " WHEN
RECOVERY OPS START.

*I recorded in my notebook a suggested code of signals.*

wrote down the instructions. 'One charge every hour would be dropped by the support ship until rescue operations were started, when three charges would be dropped'. A charge is a small explosive like a hand grenade, which is dropped over the side by the support ship and explodes when 20 feet under water. This could be heard miles away by our underwater telephone.

When finally we did make contact towards midday, I passed these ideas along with the state of our oxygen supply, our lithium hydroxide canisters, and the voltages of all the batteries. Passing such suggestions was actually a waste of effort and oxygen, as there were enough experts in the *Hecate* above to worry about these things while breathing all the good air they needed. In any case communications improved slightly very soon after this.

Thursday dragged on without incident. It was a matter of waiting for *Voyager* to arrive, and conserving our oxygen supply. The steady drips of condensation from the walls of the sphere had become accepted and were no longer a worry. I was still a little concerned about our oxygen consumption, which at that time was .3 litres/min/man; this was about .05 litres more than the rate calculated by the surface to allow until Saturday afternoon to complete the rescue; down on the ocean bed we were not aware of these precise calculations. Nothing was likely to happen before midnight, so we made further determined effort to relax completely and not talk. Every unneeded word spoken would mean so many fewer seconds for the rescue, while every wasted movement might cut off minutes. Even thoughts and worries could steal survival time.

During the afternoon I began to get cramp in the legs. It was not really painful, but as we were now lying together to share warmth, it meant a disturbance every time it happened. The only way to get rid of it was to straighten both legs or turn over. Roger was very tolerant.

The effects of a $CO_2$ level continuously higher than normal were beginning to show. It was painful to sit up every half hour and search for the oxygen supply, and even to talk on the underwater telephone. The timers, when they went off, became particularly annoying, with a very sharp ringing noise. It was like lying in bed during the winter in a cold room, suffering from 'flu, with an alarm clock going off every half hour to remind you of the reality of staying alive. Our reality was a little difficult to comprehend and face up to, as the easiest thing was to do nothing;—just turn over and sleep through the next timer, and then no more noise to worry about. If we did this it would be more difficult to wake up the next time, after yet another 30 minutes of $CO_2$ had taken its effect.

Up on the surface they sensed that we were losing interest in events, and at 9 pm on Thursday evening gave us the cheerful news that *Voyager* was only four hours away and making good time. They were very concerned that we might have expected her earlier, as had been previously reported, but by now an extra hour or two meant nothing to us, as our routine was confined to half hour patterns. Day or night were as one.

Yet day and night had great significance to the rescue teams. Through the day's passage to the scene of the sinking, preparations had been made to get all systems absolutely ready for the launch of *Pisces II* the moment *Voyager* arrived above us. For many of the rescuers there had been no sleep at all since the Tuesday night, whilst our particular operations team had been involved since our dive had begun at 1 am on Wednesday morning.

At 11.20 pm on Thursday evening, as preparations were nearing completion to launch *Pisces II* on the first mission to the seabed, our underwater telephone spoke. '*Vickers Voyager* is in sight', was the first message then '*Pisces II*, with Des D'Arcy and Roy Browne will be coming down for you shortly'.

These messages were as good as a pint of fresh air and a glimpse of genuine daylight. Our trusted support ship, who had left the previous day in such a flurry of noise as she disappeared over the horizon, was back in sight from our surface guardship and only one hour's steaming away. It was very dark on the surface, but activity was intense.

The first task was to transfer Ralph Henderson back to *Voyager* so that he could maintain the link of communication; then the duties of support ship could be transferred from *Hecate* to *Voyager*. David Mayo was to remain in *Hecate*, the ship which was to continue playing a vital part in the rescue operation.

For the third time in 36 hours, simple instructions came over the underwater telephone; but this time with a difference. '*Pisces*, *Pisces*, this is *Hecate*. *Voyager* will be calling you shortly and then taking over control'.

We would expect a quick change round as *Voyager* had fixed transducers in her hull and all she had to do was get in position and give us a call. This she did and a new voice came over our loudspeaker at 1 am.

'*Pisces*, this is *Voyager*. Communications check over'.

'Loud and clear', we replied 'Welcome back'.

'Roger (not our own names, but a form of acknowledgement). We shall be launching *Pisces II* shortly'

At last things were happening. Soon our sister submersible *Pisces II* would be in the water above us and starting down.

*Taken aboard* Pisces *some time later, this shows how I slept with my head beside the $CO_2$ indicator and the timer strapped to my wrist.*

# 8. Search on the Seabed

The feeling of relief that *Voyager* was back remained with us down below as preparations were made on the surface. I could imagine the atmosphere onboard the *Voyager*. Our original team, led by Ralph Henderson who was by then back with it, was working flat out alongside a large number of pilots, divers and technicians who had joined at Cork. Actually no-one had slept, changed, or sat down for a regular meal; divers had remained in their wet suits, covered by foul weather clothing; pilots were in overalls, and others were in the same clothes as they had worn two days before.

In everyone's mind was *TIME*. Forty-eight hours had passed since our dive had started, and in another twenty-four the life support supplies in *Pisces III* would be running out.

'Time', reflected aloud Sir Leonard Redshaw, Chairman of Vickers Shipbuilding Group, when he heard of the accident. 'The history of submarine accidents is the running out of time'.

He and Gregory Mott, Managing Director of Vickers Oceanics Ltd, had been involved from the start; both were to monitor expertly every move that was being made out at sea. Sir Leonard's direction to Peter Messervy had been 'Get everything you may possibly need—everything. Assume that the odds are against you'.

That policy had been carried out to the letter. The odds were mounting up against the rescuers. The weather was bad. Even under hard-pressed conditions on charter, no operations controller would contemplate launching a submersible in the state which prevailed that night: the swell and waves were too high and and the wind too strong. Every man in a responsible

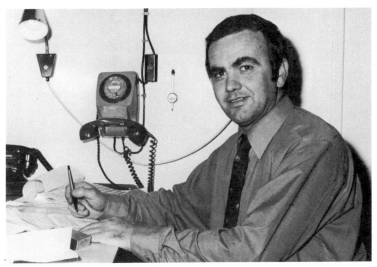

*Captain Len Edwards was Master of the* Voyager *at the time of the rescue operation.*

position from the captain, Len Edwards, to the operations manager, pilots and divers, was aware of the risk in that weather. Yet no thought was given to delaying the first launch of *Pisces II*.

In the whole operation probably the item most vulnerable, both from weather and from mechanical failure, was the *Gemini*—an inflatable rubber boat used to carry the divers and marking buoy equipment in the launch and recovery sequences. Although incredibly robust, it was liable to turn over when high winds blew over heavy seas; then its outboard engines were constantly subject to spray, rain and violent motion, so however well they had been serviced, they could be temperamental just at the time they were most needed. Thus two complete *Geminis* with outboards were ready at all times during submersible operations.

One hour after midnight, at 1.07 am to be precise, all was ready to launch *Pisces II*. Clutched in her mechanical arm was the toggle, a specially designed grapnel which was to be inserted into the aft hatch of *Pisces III;* once in and opened, it would be unable to come out. Attached to the toggle and lashed to *Pisces II's* side was a buoyant rope eight inches in circumference.

91

*Voyager* moved carefully into position besides the buoys marking our position. There the captain gave instructions to launch the *Gemini*, which is the initial action in the launch process.

The curtain was up, but an essential actor refused to play a small but vital part when nothing on earth could persuade the first outboard engine in the *Gemini* to start. At first a few minutes for temperament were acceptable, but in such heavy seas it was extremely difficult for the *Voyager* to remain precisely in the launching position.

This obstinate mood of the engine seemed infectious as two more outboards failed to start. After the long wait, middle-of-the-night frustration mounted, while for a whole hour all effort turned from the submersible to a small rubber boat and its outboard engines. The first incident in the rescue operation showed with cruel force that nothing could be left to chance; it was to be a long and hazardous operation.

At last, and it was after 2 am by then, one outboard became serviceable. *Voyager* moved into position once more.

The two pilots in *Pisces II* had been sitting in their submersible waiting as patiently as they could, checking and rechecking all systems; Des D'Arcy and Roy Browne were the two most experienced operational pilots in Vickers Oceanics and had learnt to leave nothing to chance.

The two of us in *Pisces III* also waited, but the hour's delay perhaps passed more quickly for us than for them. We sent a message to the surface, indicating what we thought was our position in relation to the pinger; we knew the exact depth of water where we had last deployed it,—1625 feet. *Pisces III's* depth gauge read 1575 feet, so if the depth increased slowly to the west, as we had found during our dive, then at a rough estimate we were somewhere possibly just east of the pinger, and close to the cable on which we had been working.

As we were inevitably immobile and also stuck on end, we had no means of assessing the direction of the pinger. Had we been able to do this, a rescue submersible could easily find us, as it could use its directional location equipment to go to the pinger and then head in the opposite direction to our bearing of the pinger. Over the last two days Roger and I had listened almost continuously to this pinger, and it sounded as if we were almost on top of it. But although sound may not be able to travel great distances in water, it can be loud and distinct to the human ear when nearby.

There was no doubt that our judgement and ability to think logically were becoming impaired by the poor conditions in *PIII*. After telephoning our lengthy message about the pinger, both of us found ourselves listening intently for the sound of *PII* entering the water, and this concentration was literally burning up our oxygen supply. As I am by nature lazier than Roger, I rested a hand on his shoulder to make him lie down while he watched intently for the lights of the rescue submersible on that first dive.

At 2.14 am on Friday morning *Pisces II* left the tossing deck of *Voyager* and entered the water. Sixteen minutes later, when her towline had been released and she had started to submerge, we heard with relief the first communications check between her and the ship, '*Voyager*, *Voyager*, this is *Pisces II*. Communications check, over'. There was no stopping us now; lying back in the dark we were eagerly waiting to join in and make it a three-way conversation between the *Voyager*, *PIII* and *PII*.

*PII* had nearly a quarter of a mile to travel towards the seabed; she was carefully clutching her toggle while the rope was being fed out slowly from the deck of the *Voyager*.

'One hundred feet . . . . . . 150 feet . . . . . . 200 feet'. We listened to Des D'Arcy calling out his depth in *PII* to *Voyager*. His voice became clearer as he left the turbulent waters of the surface. Roger sat up again to watch for the lights and I lay with my hand clutching the microphone of the underwater telephone. 'Three hundred feet . . . . . . 400 feet . . . . . . 500 feet'. All sounded well and the voice, although distant, was becoming louder.

Our first indication in *PIII* of the rescuers' presence would be her lights faintly lightening the water, as if seeing a distant car approaching at night on a twisting mountain road. Our eyes had become completely accustomed to the intense dark, and apart from using the steadily dimming torches to check gauges and locate equipment, the light from the luminous depth gauges above our heads was enough to show dim shapes within *PIII*, including each of us. We should be able to see her lights a long way off.

'Nine hundred feet . . . . . . 1000 feet'. *Pisces II* was approaching the bottom, but she was having trouble communicating with the surface. Several times *Voyager* asked for her depth to be called out again. Ironically *PIII*'s communications were better with *Voyager* at that time so I decided to join in.

'*Voyager*, this is *Pisces III*. *Pisces II* reports her depth as 1000 feet. Over'. 'Roger *PIII*, thank you?', and then Des d'Arcy and I had our first direct communication, although very distorted.

'Good . . . hear . . . voice. Will . . . you shortly'. It was not difficult to guess the full words of the message, but little did we know that at the time she was probably quite a long distance away from us, drifting unavoidably in the sub-surface currents on the descent. The only indications we had were that Des D'Arcy's voice, although clear, did not sound close, and also that Roger had seen no sign of lights in the water outside.

'Eleven hundred feet . . . . . . 1200 feet.' The three-way conversation continued; then we heard nothing more for several minutes.

In *Pisces II* at 1250 feet Des D'Arcy and Roy Browne heard the sickening sounds of the lashings breaking away,—the lashings that held the lift line to *PII*'s side. The length of line to reach this depth had quite substantial buoyancy, as every hundred feet more floating rope forced below the surface added to the upward pull, so that although there was plenty of slack as it was fed out from *Voyager* the bottom end was tending to tug *PII* back to the surface. The line had been lashed only lightly to the rescue craft so that once the toggle had been inserted in the correct position she could back away, breaking the lashings to leave the line attached to us. Yet these lashings were being pulled away by the buoyancy of the line before she had reached the bottom.

Des D'Arcy knew he should report this fact to the surface immediately, but he also knew that we were listening intently to every word and he could appreciate what disappointment this would bring us.

Would the last few lashings hold? Des and Roy felt fairly certain they could not and a few seconds later the issue was firmly decided, as the pull of the buoyant line bent the metal arm of the manipulator holding the toggle.

94

*Pisces II* was temporarily useless as a rescuer. Indeed her own situation was becoming hazardous but Des reported calmly to the surface 'Voyager, Voyager, this is *PII*. The lashings are breaking away . . . depth 1250 feet. Over'. That was all.

I heard this, but the message and tone of voice from *Pisces II* did not show any fear or disappointment, and no such feelings were transmitted to us. OK I thought. The lashings are breaking away, but fortunately we had no clear idea of what the lashings were holding or how difficult the situation was.

*Voyager* came back immediately, as if sensing the situation 'Roger, *Pisces II*. Continue to the bottom and await instructions. Over'. That was great. She was still coming down, and would find us shortly. The problem of lashings breaking away quickly left our minds, but of course to the pilots of *PII* it was a bitter blow. Their objective had been to place the toggle in our aft sphere with a line attached strong enough to lift us off the bottom. This was no longer possible.

'Fourteen hundred feet . . . . . . 1500 feet'. *Pisces II* continued down. Communication had improved slightly between *PII* and *Voyager*, so somehow I sensed that it was better to keep quiet and dropped out of the three-way talk.

We were both very tired, and because of the excitement the level of $CO_2$ in the atmosphere had increased sharply. So that we could listen to the underwater telephone better, the scrubber had not been run for the past 45 minutes. We were once again forgetting our primary task—relax, keep still, use little oxygen, and wait patiently.

It had taken *PII* over an hour to reach the bottom, but at 3.40 am she was down and operating her sonar equipment to try and locate us. We had a small device fixed to the outside of *Pisces* called a transponder which would respond with its own signal when interrogated by a beam or sound in the water; this could be picked up on a small television screen by the submersible operating her sonar.

By then there were signs that *PII* might be some distance away from us. In *PIII* we could only hear faint transmissions of her sonar. 'Tick . . . tick . . . tick'; the sound was like a clock as it swept the ocean floor in search of the target.

The sonar can operate in two ways; one is the transponder

mode already explained, and the other is the transmission mode, which uses the principal of pushing out a beam of sound into the water in a certain direction, then waiting for the beam to be bounced back from a large object, like a rock or another submersible. The sonar must be operated very skilfully to obtain the best results; by moving the submersible round, while lifting the beam up and down electronically, every portion of the seafloor nearby must be investigated before the submersible can move off and search from another position.

Des and Roy carried out these procedures with detailed care while we listened to the faint 'tick . . . tick . . . tick'. *Voyager* waited 1575 feet above, thrown about by rough seas, and surrounded by other vessels. It was obviously vital to locate us positively as soon as possible. At last a very faint echo was picked up on *Pisces II*'s sonar in the transponder mode at 6000 feet,—one mile, which is a long way in submersible operations.

Before anything could be done about that, yet another major setback demanded immediate action. This time *Pisces II* had a leak. Water was coming into the main sphere which housed the two pilots, so if it turned into a big leak, *PII* would be much worse off that we were in *Pisces III*. Fortunately it was only a slight leak with sea water coming in through one of her penetrators, which had failed to seal correctly. However you can't take chances at 1500 feet, so she had to surface immediately for the fault to be put right.

We did not hear the messages about this between *Pisces II* and the *Voyager*, which was just as well. Either communications were bad or the pilots of *PII* had once again kept their feelings out of their voices.

Very rapidly *PII* became positively buoyant and left the sea-bed bound for the rough seas above. 'Off bottom' was the report from Des d'Arcy. We listened sadly to the depth being called out. '700 feet . . . 600 feet . . . 500 feet.' Then the voice faded and only the sound of our pinger close by could be heard above the background noises of the waves, and of sea creatures going about their business.

At 4.18 am *Pisces II* reached the surface. It was two hours and twenty minutes after starting her dive. Luckily our senses must have been partly numbed. We were left to ourselves again down in the depths. Familiar voices were no longer to be heard and maybe we could rest a little. It all began to seem a little unreal. Our second $CO_2$ canister was also giving up the ghost. Twenty-nine hours (or a total of 58 man hours as there were two of us breathing out) subjected to a humidity of nearly 100% had saturated the pellets of Lithium Hydroxide so that they could no longer absorb the $CO_2$. *Pisces II* had left us, headaches were painful, and the level of $CO_2$ was high. The easiest solution would be to turn over and go to sleep.

Once again the rescuers in *Voyager* seemed to sense the situation. '*Pisces III* this is *Voyager*. We are having slight trouble with *PII*'s manipulator arms. Nothing serious. We shall be launching *Pisces V* shortly. Standby for fifteen minute communication checks. Reply by two clicks on your transmitter'.

These instructions cleared the air in more ways than one. Our spirits were raised by the news of *Pisces V* and fifteen minute communication checks would keep us awake. Just clicking our transmitter without talking would save oxygen, and the clicks could be picked up by the sensitive listening equipment mounted on the *Voyager's* hull.

*Pisces II* was recovered successfully in really difficult conditions, then as soon as the submersible was safely secured on the after deck of *Voyager* engineers and technicians descended upon the damaged manipulator and investigated the leaking penetrator. There were also serious discussions on the difficulties of carrying buoyant rope to below 1000 feet.

Meantime the problems and objectives were clearly defined. A rescue submersible must commence her dive right on top of *PIII*'s position; she must descend to the seabed as quickly as possible carrying a line attached to a lifting device which did not effect her manoeuvrability or hold her off the bottom. Once on the seabed, she must locate *Pisces III*, attach the line, and then be able to move away leaving the line firmly attached.

At least Pisces II's dive had gained valuable information for Peter Messervy and Bob Eastaugh, the operations manager. So disappointment was put aside, as *Pisces V* was almost ready to go down.

At 4,30 am, the underwater telephone was turned up for the fifteen minute check, when the persistence of the pinger sounded annoyingly loud. Could we turn the sound down a little? Or maybe turn it off altogether between the checks? Then there would be complete silence and darkness . . . and sleep. We turned it down, and missed the very next communications check. 'Wakey . . . wakey, *Pisces*', came a cheerful voice half an hour later. We were not playing our part in the rescue operation but drifting away mentally.

*Pisces V* was launched at 5.45 am. Her basic design was very similar to *Pisces II* and *III*, but her buoyancy system differed slightly; this meant that she took longer to leave the surface and begin the descent once she had been released from the support ship tow-line. This was an obvious disadvantage when rough seas and swell would cause her to drift out of position.

Len Edwards, the captain of *Voyager*, once again approached the buoys marking *PIII*'s position. His instinct told him where we were beneath the waves, although at times *Voyager's* sonar indicated differently. He had hardly left the bridge of his ship for over two days, while his officers and crew were either on watch or assisting in the preparations for launching submersibles. No-one was concerned with what time of day it was, but all were aware that any delay or mishap added minutes or hours to the operation. Time was on no one's side.

As *Pisces V* left the surface and made her way beneath the waves, an unfamiliar voice with a Canadian accent echoed over our loudspeaker. 'This is *Pisces V*, left surface OK, depth 50 metres'.

Depth 50 metres? These were the words that slowly brought home the reality to us that a second submersible, which only 36 hours ago had been on the other side of the Atlantic, was now above and on the way down. We did not know that she had clutched in her manipulator a special snap hook, which was an exact replica of the one used in the previous *Pisces III* rescue off Canada. This time the plan was to attach the device to our lifting gear.

'Depth 200 metres . . . AOK'.

How many feet in a metre? I wondered vaguely and this simple sum proved quite an effort although three times 200 and add a few feet was all that the mind needed to calculate. We listened as she slowly made the descent. It took about 30 minutes.

The build-up of $CO_2$ was quicker with the new excitement as a submersible was once again on the way down. This time we made a real effort to keep calm; we also put off the process of changing to the last $CO_2$ canister, as it was essential to eke out our supplies to the limit of time.

At 6.15 am *Pisces V* reached the bottom and we exchanged a few words with her. She also sounded some distance from us but no trouble had been experienced with her lift line. Our spirits rose as she commenced her search.

'Tick ... tick ... tick'. The sonar started an all round sweep from her landing position. Within ten minutes a faint transponder target was picked up fairly close and she moved off to investigate, creeping along the seabed. Very soon it was established that this was not *Pisces III* so she stopped again to search with the sonar.

For six long hours *Pisces V* searched in vain.

It was almost unbelievable to all that she was unable to locate us. No one knew then that by a one in a thousand chance we had landed stern first in a slight hollow, where we were hidden from the searching sonar, except at short range. The problem was developing into a needle in a haystack situation, or trying to land a penny on top of a sixpence in the deep end of a swimming pool.

The searching submersible *PV*, criss-crossed the ocean floor investigating each possible target. Every trick known to the submariners was used. At one stage I asked her at what depth she was searching; '460 metres' came the reply (1508 feet). The pilot then asked us for a long count, as she turned west into deeper water.

'Count to 50, we shall try and get a bearing', came the instructions in the now familiar Canadian accent.

As I counted over the underwater telephone *Pisces V* slowly turned in her position, listening intently on the headphones of her underwater listening equipment. *Pisces III* was acting like a pinger herself, sending out a steady signal, so that the rescue craft could listen for it to sound loudest, this would give her our rough direction. However, unlike the pinger, a voice becomes muffled and lost in the sea, so it is almost impossible to establish when the signal is loudest. She tried time and again. We counted, and quickly became short of

breath. This talk and effort for us was fast using up our oxygen, but it was certainly worth a try. Sadly it failed and *Pisces V* was unable to get any further hint of where we lay.

At 7.30 am, after consultation with the *Voyager, Pisces V* headed for the pinger on the cable, which she could also hear loud and clear. Try as we could to concentrate and keep in touch with events, Roger and I were losing track. All the effort from the *Voyager* was being directed at *Pisces V* and her search, and we in *Pisces III* drifted off to sleep between intermittent communication checks. At one time I awoke, convinced that I could hear *PV* quite close; at another we listened to a distant conversation between *PV* and the surface about two pingers now heard on the seabed, one very distant.

Around 8 am *Pisces V* arrived at our own pinger, which two days before had been left beside the cable on which we had been working.

The sea was playing tricks on us all. Above, the waves were high and stormy. Below we lay hidden in our little hollow, while a puzzled submersible desperately followed the echoes and noises of targets that would vanish on approach.

Time crept by relentlessly.

While the seabed search had been going on, *Voyager* had been operating her own sonar, and aided by the instincts of the captain and others, knew precisely where we were beneath them. At 9.47 am, the *Voyager* decided to call off *PV's* search and bring her to the surface. Once there the plan was to tow the submersible into this exact position.

*Pisces V* left the seabed. Another few hours had passed and the $CO_2$ canister was only just giving a pretence of keeping the $CO_2$ level at an acceptable limit in *PIII*. We still delayed changing it, frightened of the physical effort required and hating the thought of getting down to the last can.

# 9. A Song for Survival

When *Pisces V* surfaced on that Friday morning the divers had the problem of connecting the towing lines in rough seas. Still clutched in her manipulator was the snap hook and also the lifting line which had been gathered in as she made the ascent, but was floating over the surface. At all costs this line had to be kept slack, so as not to tear it out of the grasp of the PV as she was towed back to *Voyager*.

Meantime, the world's press had gathered to find out what was going on; thus in addition to *Voyager*, *USS Aeolus* and *HMS Hecate*, there were gathered several smaller vessels, mainly fishing trawlers carrying representatives of the press.

The trawlers, one in particular, crept closer and closer, eager to find out the facts. The noise of the high revving engines and turning propellors seriously interfered with communications and the ships seemed unaware that lines and buoys covered the surface above our position. On several occasions Len Edwards requested on VHF radio the trawler to keep clear. His requests were ignored, so he abandoned his polite tone and reverted to more seamanlike language. This too was ignored. Even after a helicopter had taken off from the *Hecate*, displaying a blackboard with simple instructions to keep clear, the trawler maintained her position in and around the scene of operations.

An additional problem had come to light, as *Pisces V*'s gyro compass was wandering for some reason, so failed to show a true direction to the Canadian pilots. It would have burned up precious time to recover the submersible and fix the compass, while getting her in and out of the water from the tossing deck

*Divers preparing* Pisces V *for towing to the estimated position over* Pisces III.

of *Voyager* was a hazardous operation in itself: so it was safer to tow her to over *Pisces III*'s estimated position and hope for the best.

Despite the weather and the interfering trawlers, by 11 am on that Friday morning, fifty hours after the accident, *Pisces V* was on her way down again, still clutching the line and snap hook in her manipulator. Everyone waited, nervous and on edge, while she made the slow descent.

In *Pisces III*, we had set the timers for a communications check, so awoke to hear the Canadian voice calling out the depth. '150 metres . . . 200 metres'.

I turned to Roger and grinned. 'Here they come again, third time lucky, I bet'.

No reply. He was in a great deal of pain and lying face down, although for the last few hours he had not mentioned the pain. The $CO_2$ was having a bad effect and I was worried. I tried again. 'Rog, *Pisces V* is on the way down for another try. Won't be long now'. He reached out and held onto my hand. He was OK.

At that time the instrument which showed the $CO_2$ concentration in the atmosphere read just under 2%, but it was obviously under reading.

*Pisces* carried as part of the emergency equipment a small test kit which could give the percentages of $CO_2$ and $O_2$ in the sphere; I switched on my torch and found this quite easily as it was one item we had restowed soon after arriving on the bottom. The torch was very dim, but I managed to draw air into a small tube, where it discoloured the substance inside more or less depending on the amount of $CO_2$. The reading was $3\frac{1}{2}$%, which was a great deal worse than the instrument reading of 2%, and well beyond the accepted limit.

I decided to hang on a little and if *Pisces V* was successful in finding us this time I would change to the last $CO_2$ canister and open the can of lemonade. Neither of us had felt very hungry during the last 48 hours, but had nibbled at a glucose biscuit from the emergency pack; the small amount of coffee left after the last dive had lasted well, so this and the condensation running down the inside of the sphere had kept us from feeling too thirsty. One effect of excess $CO_2$ is a dry taste in the mouth, and we had once or twice eyed the single can of lemonade hopefully. But this was our 'champagne' and reserved for a special occasion.

A Canadian voice from *Voyager* was talking to *Pisces V* on her way down, acknowledging the depth reports. I listened to the distorted voices over the loudspeaker. 'This is PV. Depth now 300 metres AOK, over'. . . . 'Roger, PV, out'.

For a minute I experienced a feeling of loneliness and hostility towards these voices. Why isn't one of the Oceanics team talking to us? Had *Voyager* left? Surely *Pisces II* should be coming down now with Des and Roy. They would find us. Angrily I turned over in a hurry and knocked one of the precious timers off the ledge and down into the bilge. This brought me to my senses with a jolt.

Using the torch I began to look for the timer. Over an inch of water had collected in the bottom of the sphere and there was a filthy mess of broken equipment, loose wires and scraps of food. The timer had disappeared into this, and bending down to look for it I noticed that the air in the bottom of the sphere was particularly foul, as the heavy $CO_2$ was collecting in the bottom of the sphere. I searched for some time and eventually found the timer lying in an inch of water near the hatch. The search had been thoroughly unpleasant and gave me a splitting headache, so I tied the timer to my wrist with a piece of wire and tried it out; luckily the bell still worked, with its harsh rasping note.

By 10.45 am *Pisces V* had reached the seabed and started operating her sonar once again. It was difficult to tell whether it sounded closer than the last time and during the first careful sweep around no likely sounding echoes had been picked up by the Canadian pilots on their sonar. The voices of the two pilots, however, sounded confident and expectant.

'*Pisces III*, this is *Pisces V*, do you hear me . . . . . . over'. Yes we did, clearly.

'Try a long count or sing a song, we will try and get a bearing, over'.

Here we go again, I thought. Annoyed, I reached for the loud-speaker, the headache from my excursion into the bilge still persisting Sing a song. Were we now going to play games on the seabed? But, awake once more, I began to realise that there was some point in his request. A song, especially in a high pitched voice, would give a clearer noise than normal speech and possibly a better bearing. My last long count had become a dull steady noise echoing out over the seabed and had proved no good to anyone.

Which song? I could not think of a title. I knew where we were on the seabed. I was convinced we were somewhere just east of the pinger and close to the cable, so it was only a matter of telling the submersible this once more and she would find us.

I started to sing my song about where we were. No specific tune came out. I went on and on, getting out of breath. 'Here we are, here we are, somewhere near the cable, must be near the pinger, depth is one thousand five hundred and seventy five feet . . . . . . come and find us, come and find us.'

Hide and seek on the seabed. To the fishes and creatures of the sea, it must have sounded a weird game.

I stopped to catch a little breath and was just about to continue singing, intoxicated by events. Before I could go on again, *Pisces V* came over the loudspeaker once more. Roger

*PIII*, that's fine, we have a vague direction. Standby'.

A vague direction. Could this be right? At last the searchers might have a scent. The sound of the sonar echoed out around the seabed. Tick . . . tick . . . tick . . . TICK . . . TICK . . . tick . . . tick. I could hear the sonar passing over us and being sent back. The loud ticks meant that we were sending back an echo. I could not believe it.

The ticking sonar came round again. "Now' I shouted as the loud ticks crossed us. *Pisces V* understood. The pilots quickly reverted the direction of the beam and swapped back across us. Tick . . . tick . . . **TICK** . . . **TICK** . . . 'Now'! tick . . . tick . . . They were onto us at last, but was the target being displayed on *PV*'s screen? She crept forward, sweeping back and forward in the narrow area ahead.

At exactly 800 feet off *PV* gained her sonar target. Immediately we detected a change in range scales as the sonar locked onto us. The ticking became very rapid. Roger and I sat up, still in pitch darkness, hardly daring to breathe, but still short of breath. After all this time, was it possible that we had been located.

Then quite suddenly, out of the viewing parts, we both saw a faint lightening in the waters. It became brighter and brighter. To our eyes it was like bright sunlight all round as if someone had opened a door to a dark room and flooded it with light.

Roger's emotions were clearly seen. Tears streamed down his face and as if ashamed, he buried his head on my shoulder. We shared a moment of intense relief and joy together which I shall never forget.

It was at 12.44 pm on the Friday that *PV* saw us lying stern first on the bottom of the Atlantic.

'Roger, *Pisces III*, we see you now', came the friendly Canadian voice. 'Standby, we shall be manoevring around'.

With the light shining in from *Pisces V*, we sat up and took stock of the situation. There was nothing positive we could do to help *PV* attach the snap hook to our lifting device; but we listened with intense interest as she passed a report to the surface. '*Pisces III* lying 80–85 to the vertical in soft mud, little exterior damage. After hatch opening visible'.

The time had come to celebrate with the can of lemonade. It tasted delicious, but we allowed ourselves only a few sips each before putting the can away carefully. Our morale was much improved, but I noticed that after Roger had sipped his lemonade he lay back in pain. Changing to the last $CO_2$ canister could be delayed no longer, so I started again on the laborious task of removing the top and bottom lids; this made me realise how weak and unco-ordinated I was after 60 hours of confinement in a tiny space. Together we struggled for over 45 minutes to do a normal 5 minute job, until the last remaining can was in position.

Then I pondered over our life support situation. The pressure remaining in the second oxygen bottle, which we were now using was 1800 psi. If our consumption remained the same this would last some 24 hours, or until noon on the following day, Saturday. We had squeezed the final last molecule out of the previous $CO_2$ canister, which had lasted $40\frac{1}{2}$ hours, or 81 manhours; the final canister should do as well. Therefore our oxygen supply was the critical factor.

We had been found 51 hours after the accident and at best there was 24 hours left to get *Pisces III* back to the surface. The main batteries, even at our new vertical angle, were holding out remarkably well. When the scrubber was running the metre, on the 120 volt system, read 100 volts. Low by normal standards, but adequate for our needs.

All these figures were passed to the surface while *PV* manoevred into position behind us to attach her snap hook. The light dimmed a little as she went behind us, but her presence was very near as she crept forward and gently nudged us. The shape of the seabed as it sloped into our hollow made things difficult for the pilots who tried to adopt a similar attitude to the *PIII* by adjusting trim, as our lift hook was well above the seabed. *PV*'s lights reflected back from the cloudy water, stirred up by her movement and hanging around as there was little current to carry it away.

Just 20 minutes after finding us *PV* attached the snap hook to our lifting point—a skilful job of patience by her crew. At last there was a positive link between *PIII* and the surface, with a line capable of lifting us clear of the seabed. All *PV* had to do was to back away carefully and thus break the ties that were holding the line to the submersible. Gently she backed away and the ties broke. She was almost clear when quite slowly the snap hook rolled over in our lifting device. The pilots watched with horror as the hook fell clear, then drifted into the darker waters around, with the buoyant line pulling it up from the seabed in spite of its weight. Perhaps the snap hook had not been fully closed, but at any rate the elaborately gained connection had been lost.

A submersible pilot is restricted to the speed of his manipulators and main motors, but the pilot of *Pisces V* immediately turned his craft, giving *PIII* a firm blow, and then with his manipulator just managed to grab the end of the hook before it disappeared from view. It was imperative to attach it to something before it tore out of the grasp of the manipulator, just as had already happened to *PII*. Somehow they managed to snap the hook onto the nearest projection of our craft.

All this had taken only a few hectic seconds. Then there was a pause and the pilots peered anxiously out of their view ports into the mud stirred up by the quick movements of their skids. They could just make out the dim shape of *PIII* then it cleared a bit more to show the line hooked firmly to our propellor guard.

At least a definite link with the surface had been made again, but the propellor guard was much too flimsy to take our weight, even in the calmest seas.

With bitter disappointment they realised that they must report to the surface that their mission had failed. They had found us, hooked on their line and had seen it slip off—just when success seemed in the bag.

Roger and I still knew nothing of this calamity while Bob Eastaugh, with many of his operations team around him at the back of the cramped bridge of *Voyager*, also waited patiently for news. The relief showed on all their tired faces as at last *PIII* had been found 1575 feet below them.

The friendly Canadian voice, picked up by our own listening loudspeaker, echoed loud and distorted inside our tiny sphere as it came from only a few feet away. '*Voyager*, this is *PV*. There has . . . . . . difficulty . . . . . . line to lift . . . . . . now secured to starboard propellor guard. We shall try . . . . . . it again . . . . . . point.'

It was difficult to understand what had gone wrong. All the movement, light and communication around *PIII* had made a great difference to our morale, but it was impossible not to sense further uneasiness from the garbled message. Nor was it completely clear to the men on the bridge what had happened Everyone waited anxiously for news, their tired minds at first reluctant to believe the full meaning of that message. Time slogged on heavily and all knew that Peter Messervy and Bob Eastaugh would not be able to start a lift until at least two good lines were attached to strong points on *PIII*. She would scarcely survive another crash to the bottom, so the risks with one line alone would be great.

If *PV* had really failed two more dives would be needed and there was no sign of the weather improving. In the hangar deck of *Voyager* men were working feverishly on *Pisces II*, unaware of the problems below while the ship pitched and rolled in the rising seas. Some were quite exhausted after nearly sixty hours without sleep, and persisting at the delicate work required to repair the manipulator. Tools and equipment placed on the deck around the submersible slid out of reach each time the ship lurched.

The next message we heard came from *Voyager*. '*Pisces V*, understand you have been unable to attach hook to lifting point. Stay with *Pisces III* and try to re-establish connections.'

The position was by then clear to everyone except Roger and I. However I appreciated that *Pisces V* would remain with us, and try to place the snap hook back on our lift point, and that *PII* would be preparing for the next dive.

At once it seemed much colder inside our sphere. Things were confusing after the excitement of the last hour, with the lights visible and eager hope of success. We seemed to be detached from events, as messages passed between *PV* and *Voyager*, but the voices from the seabed beside us were so loud it was impossible to understand. At first it was heartening to hear *PV* working behind us, and feel the occasional nudge as she manoeuvred. But soon this became part of the environment and of little interest because we had no idea what was going on.

Once again we relapsed into our routine of sleeping and setting the timers.

For over an hour *PV* tried to attach the snap hook to the lift point without success. Probably the task was impossible because the line was too buoyant in the water and *PIII*'s attitude on the seabed too much of a handicap. *PV*'s dive had started at 6 am that Friday morning and by 2.30 pm her main batteries were nearly flat. The pilots reported to *Voyager* that they were low on power and their newest attempt had failed.

The men waiting in *Voyager* had been expecting this news, but it was still a harsh reality when it came. Their efforts to prepare *PII* for her next dive had continued desperately while engineers and technicians had been discussing what could be done with the snap hook now attached to the starboard propellor guard of *PIII*. Surely something could be achieved with this line, which had been carried so carefully to the seabed and at least attached to the stricken submersible? A possibility arose.

A choker, or short pendant, was made for a line strong enough to lift *PIII*. This was designed to slide down the line now attached to the propellor guard. Once it had arrived the free end could be attached to our lift point, thus giving the equivalent of an uninterrupted heavy line to the surface.

This might work, but *Pisces II* was still not ready to dive. So it was decided that *PV* should remain alongside us and hope that her batteries would revive sufficiently to allow her to attach the snap hook to the lift point, if the choker got down to the sea bottom.

It was 4 pm on that Friday afternoon. Time still slipped away relentlessly while the two submersibles remained motionless on the seabed. *PV* with her batteries low and all her lights off to conserve power, was beside the upended *PIII*, which had been down there for 55 hours.

Inside *PIII* Roger's condition was worrying me as he was obviously in some considerable pain. I reached for the microphone and sent a short message to *Voyager*. 'Roger's condition has deteriorated slightly and I am a little concerned. However, he is bearing up well'.

This message sparked off a chain of events which caused a great deal of upset, confusion and disbelief to the people waiting for news back in Barrow.

# 10. The News Gets Home

Back home in Barrow the record had best be taken on by June, my wife.

'One perfectly normal Wednesday morning George Henson, the man I worked for, received a telephone call from the General Manager of Vickers Oceanics—Roger's boss. It was not the usual friendly call but a direct and urgent voice asking for Mr Henson. Sensing the gravity of the situation I passed this directly to my boss with no questions. It took little perception to realize something very serious was amiss, but the conversation was brief and gave me no clue. Mr Henson turned from me, replaced the receiver and walked away to the end of the office to the desk of another manager and good friend. They had a quick confidential talk away from others and walked back in my direction. Picking up his jacket, preparing to leave, my boss exclaimed, still with a grim countenance, 'We are going down to Oceanics—and you are coming with us'.

'This sudden statement made me realise my hunch was right —something was seriously amiss and this was to do with Oceanics—and my husband.

'I asked if there was a drama, and when out of earshot I was told quite plainly that there was a problem in Oceanics—they had a submersible on the bottom and Roger was in it. We had no further details, and so were going to Oceanics to find out.

'It was all hands on deck when the three of us reached Oceanics. The General Manager, Peter Messervy, was in the chair in the operations room speaking to the world. Canada, America, everywhere, all in an effort to organise one of the great rescues of history, all to save my Roger and his colleague,

112

whose name I had by then discovered was Roger Mallinson.

'Seeing this tremendous effort gave me the utmost confidence that all possible methods were going to be used to rescue the two Rogers. Not just one system was organised to be on the scene, but numerous. It was a wonderful experience of unity that seemed to be felt at that time; everyone working for the same end—to effect the rescue.

'Having witnessed these activities and after the causes and technicalities of the rescue had been explained to me, the three of us returned to the office—very optimistic.

'Roger had often talked about situations such as these occurring but had always given me the impression that the chances of rescue were very slim. For once I did not believe him; I couldn't, seeing all the efforts emanating from the ops room. They would be saved.

'Wednesday afternoon passed slowly. The operations had been arranged and we had to wait until at the earliest late afternoon next day, for further rescue developments.

'The transportation of submersibles from across the world went according to plan and without mishap. They all arrived on the scene late on Thursday.

'Already a whole day's supply of life-support had been used but we heard that estimates of its limits were conservative. I also knew that Roger would be remaining quiet and calm during all this so he would conserve as much oxygen as possible.

'During all this anxious time I was most attentively looked after by Mr Henson. He had suddenly become a wonderful friend and reassured me on many occasions about any points of the technicalities in the rescue that I didn't quite understand. I was staying with his family who were all kind and comforting, providing a relaxing and secure atmosphere in contrast to the rescue situation.

'During times of anxiety and worry involving perhaps the lives of loved ones, I realise now how important it is to be looked after by someone who is a friend but at the same time a person one respects and whom one trusts implicitly. Mr Henson and I developed an understanding that any new development or information received by one must be shared with the other. This included telephone conversations, when we both listened in simultaneously. So we heard the same news at the same time. Also in order to maintain one's appearance in coping with the situation no emotions must be shown. In my opinion this is vital.

'Many problems developed during the rescue operation but I still received messages from Roger saying he was well. Also messages from Oceanics assuring me of how well Roger was coping with the problem of staying alive. So long as the two boys did that, I knew they would be rescued. The greyest moment certainly came when we received a message saying that a communication had been received by the support ship *Voyager* that the condition of R. Mallinson was causing R. Chapman concern. This was like an almighty bang. One thing we had not even allowed ourselves to consider was the changing condition of the boys.

'A grim voiced Greg Mott phoned Mr Henson from the operations room in Oceanics. "George, we are receiving reports that the condition of the divers is deteriorating and that they are becoming delirious. We do not know yet whether these reports are correct, but I thought you should know the situation immediately. This condition could be due to lack of oxygen—we do not know yet. As soon as we have further information we will let you know".

'This had to be checked and clarified by my boss, who from previous reports received could not believe this latest news. And sure enough on checking, it was revealed to have only been a momentary cause for concern and actually all came from Roger's simple message from the seabed about his companion's bad headaches. Again we felt less alarmed!

'I continued my job as a secretary during all this operation, feeling it was far better to keep my mind occupied, and to be amongst the friendly reassuring characters in the office I had become acquainted with during my time with VSG. Also I was not far from Oceanics if any new developments occurred. I felt secure in the familiar atmosphere and also friends and relatives could contact me easily.

'Friday was a long day for everyone. At first the news filtering back to the base operations room in Vickers Oceanics at Barrow was full of encouraging news and hopes of early success. The telephone between Cork in Ireland and the operations room was in continuous use. Practically everyone working in Vickers was kept informed of every incident; Roger Mallinson's wife Pamela was informed by telephone of any significant event, as were his parents in the Lake District, and also my Roger's parents in Dorset.

'The phone rang in Mrs. Chapman's home in Lyme Regis where she was alone at the time. My mother-in-law is a small lady of 68 with tremendous spirit but was physically a little shocked at the time and not very strong. "Mrs. Chapman, please do not listen to the radio news bulletins at the moment. They are not correct. We will ring you back shortly with further news".

'My father-in-law, the same age as his wife, was down at the sea front in Lyme Regis where he had responsibilities running an aquarium which opens to holiday makers. He had been in the Royal Navy during the war and had always been interested in the sea, which is a common interest Roger and he share. On that Friday he had taken his radio down to the aquarium to listen to news bulletins. Mrs. Chapman knew this and was naturally worried, realising she would have to warn him not to listen to the radio. She was unable to drive, therefore she had to walk down the very steep road to the shore, take the path round the breakwater to the "Cob" and then to the harbour wall where she knew she would find her husband in the aquarium.

'She managed the journey with difficulty and told Mr. Chapman the message from Barrow. They were both reassured by the telephone messages but being so far from the scene and also not fully understanding Roger's underwater job they were naturally distressed.

'There was a strong wind blowing and the waves were beating against the harbour wall, filling the air with spray. Mr. Chapman sat at the reception desk deep in thought; the radio silent. Suddenly he froze. When mother-in-law had left the aquarium he realised she had turned right outside the door. He was sure. This led directly to the end of the harbour wall, where there was no protection and the waves were pounding onto the breakwater.

'Half running, he went outside to see his wife, her head bent against the wind, walking towards the end of the wall. Just in time she heard his warning shouts above the noise of the wind and saw, to her horror, where she was heading. Determined to return home as quickly as possible, in case more news came from Barrow, her mind had been completely preoccupied and she had no idea where she was going. There were very few people about, no-one wishing to venture out in such weather, so no-one had seen the small solitary figure walking towards the sea.

'The Chairman of Vickers Shipbuilding, Sir Leonard Redshaw, and Greg Mott, Managing Director of Oceanics, spent much of Friday in the operations room, apart from news conferences and essential business which they carried out in the main offices of the Shipbuilding Group. They heard firsthand the failure of *PII* on the initial dive, the long search and eventual success of *PV* in locating *PIII*, and then the bitter disappointment of the snap hook coming out of the lift point. However, communications were poor. There was no direct radio link between Barrow and the *Voyager*. Attempts had been made from the submarine being built in the shipyard, HMS *Sovereign*, whose powerful HF communications equipment

*Sir Leonard Redshaw, Chairman of Vickers Shipbuilding, right, and Mr Greg Mott, Managing Director of Oceanics, at a press conference. These were held three times a day during the rescue operation.*

might have been able to make contact had it not been for the hills around the town, the dockyard cranes and poor weather conditions.

'All through Friday there were many conflicting and erroneous reports on the radio. Naturally many people brought radios to the office to listen but they were so misleading that they were a disadvantage instead of an advantage.

'Sir Leonard was angered when he heard reports of a trawler interfering with the rescue operations and the reporting of false statements in the press. He was not a man to mince words. Chairman of one of the most successful shipbuilding groups in the country, a Vickers man for many years, he had been part of a tough industry all his life. He had given whole-hearted support to Vickers Oceanics since it had started operating submersibles commercially; he knew now the company had a serious problem on its hands and he also knew the chances of success. "This will be the deepest submarine rescue in history if successful" reflected Sir Leonard.

'At the next press conference he gave news of *Pisces V*'s failure to attach the snap hook. "We are having difficulties and time is running out. The weather is bad. An additional hazard is the presence of fishing trawlers in the area, interfering with communications seriously between the support ship and submersibles, and passing false information ashore to the press for publication. If we fail, these trawlers will be a major contributing factor".

'Friday night for me was bleak. Mr. Henson and I worked late, clearing the post and so forth in an effort to eke out the hours before better news came in. It was after 8.15 when we went down to Oceanics to discover there were no further developments or encouragement, so we slipped away quietly to have a bite to eat. For once we could not even find anything to talk about; it all seemed to have been said. We returned later to Oceanics to find, yet again, no further developments. The atmosphere there was understandably depressing, so we decided to go away and each get some much needed rest.

'On the way home we called in at the house of a friend who was keeping a watch on Roger's and my cottage and feeding the cats. Until I saw her drawn, worried face, I suppose I had not realised how this episode was affecting people other than myself. Jinny's look of deep concern told me without doubt that other people shared the same feeling that I had inside. It was difficult to be confident about the rescue because at this point nothing definite had been achieved; yet I felt it was my duty to be cheerful and to assure her that Roger would be brought up.

'One thing had really been bothering me all the time the boys were trapped on the seabed. The problem in my mind was how they were managing to relieve themselves down there. I was taken down *PI* just so I could see for myself the type of environment, and when inside I plucked up courage and asked the question. In technical terms, I was told it was just like aircraft pilots—they had special bags for the purpose. I felt immediately thankful for the information.

'However that was the next day when things were brighter. Meantime on Friday night I must admit to feeling miserable. With so little progress in the rescue it was difficult to remain confident. I went to bed with a very heavy heart but still hoping with all my might that everything would be all right.

# 11  A New Emergency

Out at sea with the light fading over the turbulent water, there was a certain uneasiness. *Pisces II* was still not ready for her next attempt. The third night of rescue operations had begun and with it brought frustration, mishap and fatigue. The rescue ships clustered around the marker buoys which could be seen from time to time in the rising seas. The operations manager knew that his team would have another long night ahead of them, and operations at night are twice as difficult as by day; they demand more of men and machines with additional hazards. For instance it would be easy to lose touch with a diver, or for an outboard on a Gemini motor boat to fail, and either would lead to precious hours being wasted in search and recovery. Thus in normal operating when weather conditions were at all doubtful operations would be called off at dusk until daylight.

However, this was not a normal operation. One rescue submersible was already 1,575 feet below the sea surface, waiting patiently besides *PIII* while resting her batteries and possibly mustering enough power for a further attempt with the snap hook. At least she could act as a beacon for another rescue submersible, because *PV* was fitted with a pinger which she herself could turn on and off, giving a valuable bearing, and making the search relatively easy.

The work continued on *PII*'s manipulator. The job was more complex than first anticipated as it turned out to have been so badly damaged on the first dive that eventually it had to be practically rebuilt. Luckily, during Friday afternoon relief technicians and engineers had arrived by helicopter from Cork.

119

They were men from Barrow who had been on holiday or at home at the time of the accident and as soon as they heard the news they volunteered their assistance. Since Wednesday night they had remained in close contact with the base, ready to fly out at a moment's notice. Then the call came and although some had never flown in a helicopter before, they found themselves being lowered from one to the heaving deck of a ship far out at sea.

In *PIII* I began to lose touch with events. Every time I woke, it took a few minutes before I realised what was going on. As Friday evening approached Roger felt a little better. He had slept and with the new canister reducing the $CO_2$, we had on one occasion used more oxygen from the bottle to improve the atmosphere. Communications checks were still carried out, but to us they seemed irregular and the Canadian voice from *Voyager* talking to *PV* was unfamiliar. It was still cold and certainly I began to be influenced by a growing sense of helplessness.

When awake I checked the oxygen levels too frequently. I worried also that the sphere might be leaking salt water, so continually checked the drips of water off the cold steel on the side. What was the time? Fortunately my watch was automatic so it had kept going, but it was not luminous so I could not read it.

Night was approaching. Roger related later that on one morning he was able to detect a very faint lightening in the water as the dawn broke a quarter of a mile above. To me it was still pitch black. I slept through several half hourly periods, Roger operating the scrubber switch and bleeding in the precious oxygen supply.

Suddenly a hideous whine awoke me with a start. It seemed to come from the loudspeaker and also through the hull. Roger and I stared at each other, unable to take in what it was. After a few seconds it ceased, leaving the noise of the distant pinger which had been the accompaniment to every sound since we plunged to the bottom.

Before we had had time to work out what this new noise was, we heard it again. The first time it had jolted our minds, but it needed to whine a second time before we realised what it was,—it was *PV* testing her pinger from just a few feet away.

It had been planned that *PV* should make another attempt at 5.15 p.m. on Friday, and again we could see her lights behind us. To try and attach the snap hook she was using the last dregs of power in her batteries; power was needed to manoeuvre the submersible into position, to operate the lights, and to control the manipulator.

Very quickly the small reserve of power dwindled away. She gave up only when it was unsafe to continue without leaving too little for the long journey to the surface and her final recovery.

Whilst these efforts on the seabed were in progress, another rescue ship arrived on the scene;—she was the cable ship *John Cabot*, which had remained in Cork to await the arrival by air from America of *CURV III*. This was the unmanned type of

*The cable controlled underwater recovery vehicle* CURV III *at Cork after flying from San Diego in a US Air Force plane is seen ready for transport to* John Cabot. *The aluminium frame carries two television cameras and the elaborate apparatus for moving and working deep under the ocean, all controlled from the surface.*

recovery vehicle which had already been used extensively for the recovery of things from the seabed, and gained a great reputation a few years earlier, when *CURV I* had recovered a nuclear weapon from a crashed aircraft off the coast of Spain. *CURV III* would be a valuable addition to the rescue team, so immediately on *John Cabot's* arrival, after her 150 mile dash at top speed from Cork, its experts had to be lifted by helicopter over to *Voyager* to work out plans.

Meantime *John Cabot* was requested to police small boats in the area, because *PII* would be ready for her second dive as soon as the toggle and braided nylon line were lashed to her. The *Aeolus* had offered *Voyager* a further 1,800 feet of special line, so messages were quickly passed between ships, and the small helicopter took off once again to transport the rope. Flying conditions were hazardous and *John Cabot's* log at this time recorded a moderated south-westerly gale blowing, with rough seas and a heavy swell.

The helicopter hovered above the deck of *Aelous* in the gale and attempted to pick up the enormous coil of rope. However in the haste of passing the messages a mistake had been made over the weight of the rope, so the pilot almost crashed into the sea with this excess load. Just in time he released it, but the rope was lost. Time too was lost before another rope was successfully passed at 7 pm that evening; but days later the pilot was rightly commended for his courageous flying during the rescue operations.

Soon after 7.30 pm the sky was overcast and the last of the daylight faded, yet the waiting period was over and rescue operations began to move again with *PII* completely ready to be launched.

The pilots of *PV* were still on the seabed inside their submersible, where they had been for 13 hours. They waited patiently beside us, and they too were feeling tired.

Roger and I were both losing track of time and the sequence of events completely. The half hourly ringing of the timers would not wake us thoroughly; operating the scrubber and bleeding in oxygen were becoming automatic and carried out in semi-stupor. I can remember very little about those few hours, except that it was intensely cold. During the afternoon, while in this state, I had made an infuriating bungle. It was the only

*A naval helicopter transferred the special line from* HMS Aelous *to* Voyager.

time I had crouched to relieve myself, using a plastic bag, as Roger had done earlier. Carelessness, cold, and a spinning head had made me so clumsy that I missed, which is not a particularly pleasant incident to relate in this story, however it must be told to give a true picture. For hours afterwards the air was particularly foul, as the damp pellets in the scrubber unit had little effect in absorbing the smell.

At 7.50 pm *Voyager* launched *PII* in the roughest conditions she had operated submersibles during her two years at the task; yet the whole thing passed us by. There really was a heavy swell, and those who have been to sea in small boats will know that waves look twice as high at night. In a small rubber craft like the Gemini it was difficult enough struggling to pick up the diver after the launch, without having also to worry about being overturned.

Voyager *launched* PII *in the roughest conditions she had operated during her two years at the task. Within a few minutes a new emergency arose as* PII *water alarm shrieked at her pilots.*

Then calamity struck again. *PII* was only just below the surface when the water alarm sounded, shrieking at the two pilots.

It seemed quite incredible to Des and Roy that this should be a genuine alarm. Surely, they felt, the aft compartment could not really be filling with water after everything had been checked so thoroughly. They knew that the alarm was prone to go off at the slightest sign of damp or water, as it was designed to be sensitive. Yet the whole rescue operation was due to *PIII*'s aft compartment flooding, so perhaps it was happening to them.

At any rate they were bound to take action at once, and this meant they must surface and have the craft recovered for investigation as a matter of emergency. There was not even time to report what had happened through the underwater telephone, so the first anyone in *Voyager* knew was to see *PII* burst to the surface.

Once there, the radio could be used and Bob Eastaugh, still standing at the stem of *Voyager* after supervising the launch, anxiously heard their report. He too could not at first believe that yet another submersible was filling with water. Yet the sea was so rough that a few seconds later in steep waves her stern appeared to dip back towards the seabed. This was desperate and somehow the submersible would have to be kept on the surface, however much water was leaking into the sphere, until the heavy lift line for recovery was attached.

The *Voyager* spun round at once and prepared to recover. Meanwhile Bob ordered his men at the stern to fetch a heavy 'mine bag'; this could be inflated by the $CO_2$ bottles which were part of its package, just as some lifejackets which can be inflated by self-contained gas cylinders. Once secured, the 'mine bag' would help keep the stern of *PII* buoyant until the submersible was recovered.

So those in *Voyager* had a new full scale emergency on their hands. Both *PIII* and *PV* had to be forgotten until *PII* was safely back onboard in that deplorable weather. It must have been a nightmare situation for all those responsible for the operation onboard *Voyager*.

# 12. Hooked On

Bob threw the mine bag into the water but luckily it was not needed,and after 25 minutes of frantic effort, *Pisces II* was back on board. The aft sphere hatch was removed and the technicians once again swarmed over the submersible. Every system had to be checked, so the slow process of preparing her for the next dive started once more. As the clock ticked by reluctantly, the vital hours were slipping away.

Weariness was on everyone's face and disappointment showed too. More decisions were required by those leading the rescue. At 8.15 pm that Friday evening the *CURV* system was ready to go, but the principal men involved with *CURV* were still in *Voyager* so the Gemini was launched once again to carry them across to *John Cabot*. The helicopter could not be used, as it was not equipped for night flying; but in any case it was short of fuel.

The wretched weather just would not abate. Two men who had handled the Gemini almost non-stop carried out their task like zombies; soaked through, even in fully inflatable foul weather clothing, it would not have stopped them even if it was to blow a hurricane. Bill Ransom and Ernie Foggin had passed through the zone of feeling tired and cold, like everyone else, they had beaten the weather. Over went one of *CURV*'s men to *John Cabot* in the Gemini, with a toggle, and at 9.30 pm another helicopter with fresh men arrived from Cork.

It was not until 11.30 pm, that the remaining two *CURV* people were safely transferred back to their own ship. At exactly midnight, yet another major setback was found— there was salt water in a connector of the *CURV* cable, and it

*Heavy seas soaked* CURV III *and its control van even 35ft above sea level, so the control cable connection had to be rewired.*

was estimated that it would take three or four hours to clean and repair it.

Instead of progress, events were going backwards. Surely the bad luck could not go on and on for ever. So a breakthrough must come some time? But would it be in time.

At midnight on Friday, it was 71 hours since the hatch on *PIII* had been shut and our dive commenced. So in another hour we would be on borrowed time, as *PIII*'s life support systems were designed to last a maximum of 72 hours. *PV* was still down on the seabed beside us. *PII* was not yet serviceable, and *CURV* would be delayed three or four hours.

I checked our meagre supplies of oxygen. The gauge showed just under 1,000 psi. I did not really take in that this would last at best another 12 hours, but light-headedly assumed that it would last for ever.

However the fact is we had an extra twelve hours. So the first slice of good luck had slowly, over the last two days, come our way; unnoticed by the two of us who were using up our life support, the oxygen and $CO_2$ scrubbing unit had not failed us once. Even the small electric timers worked almost every time we set them. (I still have mine, hidden away in a small box under the stairs at home.) Most important of all, we still had power from our batteries. The voltage was dropping all the time, but it was quite adequate for our basic needs, which were communication with the surface and running the scrubber.

Neither Roger nor I can remember very clearly what happened in the next ten hours. Until Friday night, we had roughly kept up with events as they happened, then things happened as in a dream and the dreams were not pleasant. The time between incidents was completely lost. We must have slept a great deal, but we were still operating the life support every half hour, or at least most of them. Who did it on which occasion, neither of us will ever know.

I remember having mixed feelings about my companion— angry sometimes that it was always I who reached over to switch on the scrubber or bleed in oxygen. The foul smell, and then a killing pain in the head would not be noticed if I did not have to get up all the time and do these things. But actually I was not the only one operating the switches, and I was only aware of the times when awake. One memory remaining is that it was damned cold.

We both came to when *PV* departed for the surface from the seabed beside us. After *Voyager* heard the news about *CURV* and that it would be delayed three or four hours, the decision was made for *PV* to return before her batteries were completely run down. By then her dive must have been one of the longest on record for a submersible of her type, as she had been in the water for eighteen hours. Just before she left, I remember listening to Commander Messervy's voice, but did not take in whether he was talking to us or *PV*; in fact it was a message to *PIII*, sending encouragement and giving us the latest news.

The one word that registered in the conversation was *CURV*. *CURV* was coming down, was going to do this and that, *CURV* will manage. I definitely panicked a little then. I knew about submersibles, and about *PV* and *PII* in particular, and what they were trying to do. OK, so they were having problems; but we could sleep, we did not have to make much effort to help, and they would find a way in the end. It was just a matter of time. Just try and keep curled up, shut out the cold, the foul air and the smell, and sleep. Sleep was great. Nothing went wrong when you were asleep. Just try and remember to set the timers and wake up.

But what was *CURV*? I had absolutely no idea, and then ignorance brought fear. *CURV* was coming down shortly. I remembered in the dim and distant past, in the back of my mind that *CURV* was possibly an unmanned vehicle of some sort, but then I wasn't sure.

Hell, did they really have a problem now? Surely we don't want a robot submersible interfering? It couldn't work where manned machines had failed.

And then *PV* said goodbye. It sounded very final. 'Thank you' I remarked and 'see you down here again soon.' The reply is firmly imprinted in my memory. Although *PV* was very close and her messages sometimes were loud and distorted, this one was very clear.

'I don't think we will be down again, *CURV* is great and will have you up before we can get back. Cheerio'. They were confident enough, but I was not.

The light dimmed as she left the bottom. There would be no more submersibles coming down, no more talk on the underwater telephone. Hell, what was going on up there. I was losing interest and depressed that we would not hear that friendly Canadian chatter again.

I was then convinced it was Saturday mid-day. We had rested all through the night and I suddenly felt quite awake. Roger was still asleep but he must be tired. I won't run the scrubber for a little while, it may wake him up. Lying there, eyes open and staring at pitch blackness, annoyed and depressed, but not tired. Maybe just a short sleep. Then wake for the next scrubbing time. Is the timer set? Roger's will be but I'll set mine as well.

'. . . this is *Voyager*, communication check over'. I woke up. Who was calling us? What was the time? 'Roger, *Voyager*, read you loud and clear, depth now 30 feet everything OK.'

That sounded like Des D'Arcy's voice again. I waited, fully awake once more, for the next message to come out of the loudspeaker. Could it be that after all another submersible was already coming down, and was it to be *PII*? It seemed like days since we had heard of *PII* but only minutes since *PV* had left our side.

In fact it was four hours, as the time was 4.10 am. The men back in *Voyager* had been fully aware of the passage of time; they were going flat out once more, both to recover *PV*, and at the same time to continue on *PII* so that everything was in perfect order. She was equipped with another toggle at the end of a $3\frac{1}{2}$ inch polyprophylene line; again lashed tightly, but not too tight. Hands and minds were cold and tired, but the job was carried out with meticulous care. They stood on the deck of *Voyager*, their latest charger disappearing beneath the waves. Hands clenched inside oily overall pockets, and praying that all would be well. Fingers crossed just for a few minutes, or clutching a damp cigarette. A brief mental relaxation on that long dark night.

It could only be brief. *PV* was back on deck. She must be made ready for another dive. The process would go on and on. Launch one, recover the other. Post dive checks, pre-dive checks, investigate and repair. A cigarette and a warm coffee out of a plastic cup.

'*Voyager*, this is *PII*, depth now 250 feet . . . over.' Roger and I both heard this. It was true: *PII* was coming down again. It seemed inconceivable. Everything seemed to be happening so quickly.

Time moved fast. It was intoxicating. Long before *PII* reached the bottom we saw her lights. She must be close. Coming down right above us. 'Depth now 1,000 feet AOK' 'Roger, *PII* out'

Inside *PIII* Roger and I were lying down, our small world once more filled with light. Our mobile discipline was no longer enforced. We had come to accept that it was no good getting up and looking out. Was there any point anyway? Maybe it was just another dive, sleep a little maybe, it was a long way down.

'Tick . . . tick . . . tick . . . tick . . . TICK . . . TICK . . . tick'. I awoke with a start. Roger was already concentrating and then at last realism dawned. *PII* was in earnest; she was already on the bottom searching for us.

In less than 40 minutes after leaving the surface, *PII* was by our side. It was a terrific achievement. She slowly and cautiously manoeuvred behind *PIII*; another ten minutes passed as this was done.

There were no more communications checks, as those on the surface were not going to disturb the concentration of the pilots in *PII*. They sensed achievement but did not dare hope for too much. Everyone knew that there was no time left for anything else to go wrong.

All around us was tenseness, but Roger and I were miles away, asleep again.

'. . . *Voyager*, this is *PII*. We have placed the toggle in the aft sphere hatch opening and confirm positive lock. Waiting for visibility to clear'.

After days of effort, bad luck and mishap, *PII* had descended quietly to the seabed, moved around the back of *PIII* and gently placed a line and toggle inside the gaping sphere. This toggle would fall open like an umbrella, and could not possibly come out. The $3\frac{1}{2}$ inch polypropylene was strong enough to lift us clear of the seabed. All this had taken less than 45 minutes. Incredible.

It sounds a simple operation. In fact it was. But the relief to the rescuers was enormous. At last they had achieved a success.

To us on the seabed in *PIII*, this dramatic incident almost passed unnoticed. Half way through *PII*'s message about the toggle, I lost consciousness again. It was good to have *PII* back. Her lights were a comfort. She could talk to the surface. We could sleep. Sleep was good too. God, it was cold though.

The one word I did catch was toggle. This was another problem, like understanding about *CURV*. As far as my mind got in working out what the toggle might be, it was probably some sort of large hook, which would catch the strong steel lip of the aft hatch opening. 'I hope we don't rock about when we get lifted', I remember thinking. 'It may come adrift, never mind, *PII* is with us.'

The toggle in fact was a folding grapnel; once inserted in the aft hatch sphere opening in *PIII*, it would open out and nothing that could be foreseen during recovery would allow it to fall clear.

*PIII*'s excess weight was estimated as between 0.95 and 1.5 tons. The toggle was designed to lift 3 tons with a large factor of safety to cover dynamic effects due to ship heave. It was specially designed by the shipbuilders in Barrow when they knew about the accident.

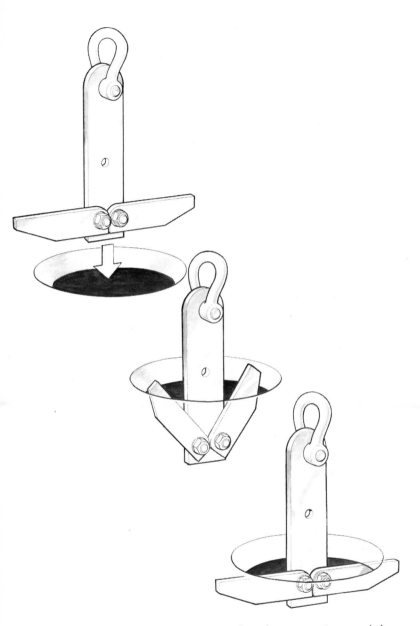

The specially designed and manufactured toggle was flown from Barrow. It was pushed through aft hatch opening by PII's manipulator, and then locked open so that it could not fall out however much Pisces III was thrown about by the sea's turbulence as she was lifted.

This is the time in all dramatic films, when two men who have spent ten days hanging by finger nails to the side of a cliff, suddenly grab the rope and are hauled to safety. They turn to each other, faces raw with cold, covered in ice, and bloodshot eyes convey a message of relief. The music adds the final touch.

Roger and I would have upset the director. We were not interested in being hauled to safety. In the back of my mind I remember the awful bucking motion when suspended beneath *Voyager* three days before. It might happen again and that was a bigger fear than staying on the bottom.

Looking back, it was a most extraordinary attitude to have. I'm sure that if we had been given two or three blankets and a drink, it would have seemed quite different.

Acute seasickness has the same sort of effects on men and women. I am fortunate and do not suffer, but by all accounts a really bad dose of seasickness is enough to make one curl up in a corner and give up. There is absolutely no desire to make an effort or help oneself. My wife had a dreadful experience the year we met when she was sailing back from the Channel Islands with two friends when a severe storm blew up. The two men fought hard to bring the little yacht safely to harbour in Southampton, but June was terribly ill and in the end was sick, or trying to be, every few minutes.

Finally the bad weather, and the fact that my wife was so ill, forced them to send up distress rockets to attract attention. An enormous Greek cargo ship, which was empty and therefore riding very high in the water, saw the flares and came to the rescue. The ship completely dwarfed the tiny yacht, and lines were lowered so that the three could be hauled up. June was helped from her dark corner out on deck. She took one look up at the bows of the ship, seemingly miles above; then she looked at the ropes which had large knots at the ends, and firmly announced she was going back to bed. The next time she was summonsed on deck the yacht was alongside a tanker and ropes had been lowered with wide leather straps attached. Thank goodness the men with her and the rescuers above, were strong enough to persuade her at last to be lifted up.

In *PIII* we were in a similar position, but fortunately for us, we did not have to do much to help ourselves. *PII* was still busy; the visibility had cleared and she could confirm that the toggle was still safe in the sphere. For some reason, probably once again because of *PIII*'s nose up attitude, our communications with the surface were better than *PII*'s.

'. . . Say again *PII*', came the voice from *Voyager* over the loud speaker. So passing on messages was something we could do to help. But what on earth were they talking about now? Keep awake and listen. 'Have soft noose in the manipulator, we will try and attach it to the lift hook'.

'. . . Say again slowly *PII*, message not understood.'

I had heard this message and relayed a disjointed sentence to *Voyager*. 'Soft noose?' I had no idea what the message relayed meant but it sounded interesting. In fact what *PII* was trying to do now was to harden up the line that *PV* had lost from her grasp and had managed to attach to the propeller guard. She was grabbing for the choker, now called the soft noose, just as *PV* had tried to do hours before; if it could be secured it would make a second lift line to the surface.

Two lift lines? At least two would be needed and fortunately the rescuers did not get excited and decide to drag us from the bottom with just one. The strains would be terrific when the submersible was getting jerked around near the surface and if that first attempt to lift was to fail there would be no time to try again; so it was a matter of belt and braces, for preference double the braces too.

Seen from the surface *PII* was busy on the seabed and that was good. The pilots in *PIII* seemed to be in reasonable shape. OK. Now what about *CURV*?

People looked up from *Voyager* and across to the *John Cabot*. Good heavens its daylight already. And what was that, a watery sun? But it wasn't. The entry in John Cabot's log at 7.05 am that Saturday morning recorded 'Strong west-south-westerly breeze, rough seas and heavy swell, overcast, intermittent rain showers'.

*CURV* was ready to be launched at 7 am. Was the line attached by *PII* back on the seabed? A quick communication established that she was experiencing the same difficulties as before. Although there was little current the semi-buoyant line was making things difficult. It was unlikely that she would be able to manage.

After a few more attempts *PII* was given permission to

leave the bottom and return to the surface. Still the enemy was time, and this could not be forgotten by the rescuers for a single moment. In the circumstances the best thing was to recover *PII* and make an attempt with *CURV* to place a second toggle in the aft sphere. One important factor was by then on *CURV*'s side; if her launch was successful, she may be able to follow the $3\frac{1}{2}$ inch line right down to the aft sphere using her own sonar. Therefore she could land close to us on the seabed, just as *PII* had done.

*PII* was recovered without difficulty as the weather at least was improving a little; and *John Cabot* was asked to station herself close to *Voyager*.

At just after 8 am Des D'Arcy climbed out of *PII* after his successful dive. There were no dramatics, as there was still much to be done. It was decided immediately that he should transfer with Bob Eastaugh to the *John Cabot* and have a look at the pictures being sent back by television as *CURV* made her attempt. He had first hand knowledge of conditions and knew *PIII*'s attitude on the seabed exactly.

*Clutched in* CURV's *manipulator was a second toggle and attached to this a six-inch braided nylon line.*

CURV *was launched into a rough sea. In air it weighs about 5,000 lbs, but afloat has slight positive buoyancy and can normally operate down to 7,000 feet.*

CURV's *vital contribution to the rescue was organised by Commander Moss, U.S.N. of SUPSALV, Commander Nielson, U.S.N. of CINCUS-NAVEUR, and Mr Earl Lawrence, the U.S. Navy's senior civilian salvage master.*

CURV's *tether cable was taped to the lift line for* Pisces III *as they went over the bows of* John Cabot.

It is not much good taking the story back to the feelings of us two inside *PIII*. From the time *PII* left our side to the time the lift commenced is almost a complete blank in my memory. In fact it was four hours. We operated our life support equipment and set the timers. Several brief seconds are remembered and I will try and bring them in to the story as they occurred.

*CURV* was launched at 9.40 am; clutched in her own manipulator was the second toggle, and attached to this a 6 inch braided nylon line. She had similar systems to a Pisces submersible, but no crew: rather like a floating bedstead which took its orders from an operator who watched its every movement on a tiny TV screen.

She followed down the line left by *PII*. After the last three days of trial and misfortune the sequence of events were so

*Transmitted by a television set from CURV on the ocean bottom this shows the second toggle actually being inserted in the aft sphere opening of* Pisces III, *while the two pilots lying in the main sphere had no idea what was going on.*

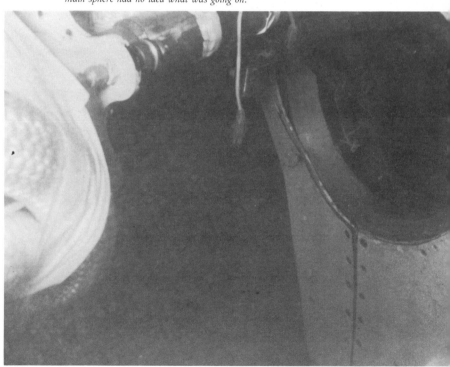

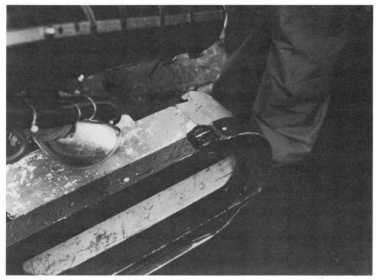

CURV's *gyro compass had been disabled so a diver's compass was strapped on to a forward runner within view of the television cameras.*

troublefree as to be almost unbelievable. This is how it went

| 9.50 am | *CURV* at 190 feet |
| 10.12 | *CURV* at 1100 feet |
| 10.30 | *CURV* homing in on *PIII* |
| 10.31 | *CURV* has visual contact |
| 10.35 | *CURV* has positive lock with toggle inserted in aft sphere opening. |

In the control van on deck, Bob and Des had watched fascinated as this took place. She landed so close to *PIII* that sonar contact was picked up immediately. As she approached and gained visual contact, Des was able to advise on the conditions, and help the operators position the robot craft exactly right for the insertion of the toggle.

And so, there we were. In six and a half hours the situation had been transformed from one of near hopelessness to a position of great prospect. Two strong lines were ready to lift us up.

# 13. 'Whatever happens we lift at 11.30'

Completely oblivious to *CURV*'s arrival on the seabed and success in placing the toggle, I remember only a loud whirring noise which seemed to last for hours. Then a garbled message '. . . whatever happens we lift at 11.30 . . .'. I did not take this in fully and went back to sleep.

The final stage of the rescue was about to begin, with all its risks and uncertainties for those in charge on the surface, who dare not delay any longer as our oxygen was nearly spent. However they had high hopes of getting us to the surface alive.

My feelings down on the seabottom were quite different as most of all I wanted to be left alone. Indeed for me going up was to be the final and most excruciating nightmare. It was no longer possible to sleep and ignore events, so it proved quite the most terrifying experience of my life.

As soon as Bob Eastaugh arrived onboard the *John Cabot* he felt that her lifting gear was particularly suitable for raising *PIII*. He had not stopped for one minute since receiving the news of the accident back on Wednesday when way out in the North Sea, yet his judgement proved to be perfectly sound. He radioed *Voyager* immediately, asking Peter Messervy's permission to carry out the lift from *John Cabot* and not from *Voyager* as originally planned.

*John Cabot*'s captain had been faced with a difficult decision. It would be a grave responsibility and the rescue, although dogged with difficulties throughout, was approaching a critical stage. The weather was still playing its part, the big swell causing his ship to pitch up and down heavily, so winching any large object from such a depth would be difficult. But his decision had been almost instantaneous and he accepted the responsibility; so, along with all the other rescuers, we owe him our lives. Like so many who were involved from other parts of the world, when everything was over his ship sailed away before Roger and I had managed to thank him personally. One day we hope to do so.

At 10.50 am on that Saturday morning, a little earlier than planned, the *Voyager* called and called us again over the underwater telephone. They made contact at last. '. . . you are being lifted now *PIII*, over.' 'Roger'. We replied. What else was there to say; we were being lifted?

Dragging ourselves out of the comatose world we had lived in for so many hours, we put on the small dome lights and stared at each other. The oxygen gauge read just under 800 psi. Perhaps this next stage would pull us to our senses and possibly relieve the severe headaches which racked our brains. The scrubber was switched on and left running while a good burst of oxygen was released into the sphere; *PIII* was being lifted so we could afford to be extravagant. Yet the fact that **WE** were actually going to be lifted at last still did not register fully in my mind; there was certainly no thought that rescue might now be just round the corner, but instead there was annoyance that we were to be disturbed.

As our eyes became accustomed to the light we had switched on the shambles in which we had been existing for the last few days showed up. I remember feeling how angry Bob Eastaugh would be when he saw the mess. His standards were always high, and his influence indirectly affected us even on the seabed; so we placed any loose gear we could in the bottom of the sphere, grovelling around rather than moving, and then jammed ourselves at opposite ends of the sphere, half sitting. I looked at Roger and we waited; the scrubber was still working and the improved atmosphere was having its effect, so our minds began to be capable of thought instead of mere habit reactions; they also became capable of anxiety again.

So we were being lifted then. Christ, what would happen when the ropes took the weight? Were the ships stationed exactly above us or would we be dragged across the seabed and turned over? Fear and excitement took charge, and we began to burn up the oxygen.

After what seemed like an age, but in reality was only a few minutes, *PIII*'s attitude slowly altered; we were being lifted by the tail, so the front end of *Pisces* fell forward. It was a gradual beginning, and the depth gauge did not alter a fraction as we were still on the bottom.

We shifted our positions as the different angles came on. Nothing was said. This was something new to us after so much inactivity.

The angle of the submersible reached about 50° and we were still on the bottom. Then there was a sharp thump and *PIII* started to drag across the seabed. 50° . . . 45° . . . 40° . . . Still on the bottom and thump, thump. I reached for the microphone of the underwater telephone, something to hold on to tight. 'I'd better tell them to stop lifting if we look like turning over' I thought.

'*Voyager*, . . . *Voyager* . . . this is *PIII* over'. My voice was almost a shout. But communications were no good. Only a whirring noise over the loudspeaker.

40° . . . 30° . . . and then the depth gauge flickered for the first time. We were leaving the bottom of the Atlantic.

I would have been happy then to be dragged 150 miles to shore and right up the beach rather than leave the bottom, for as soon as we were clear the pendulum motion started again. Quite gently at first, rocking slowly back and forth but it was too late then to alter our positions. Just hang on.

Loose gear shifted about beneath us, but the depth gauge was moving all the time slowly upwards. 1400 feet that meant 175 feet clear of the seabed. Now we were really in the swing of things, horizontal one minute and back to our old vertical position the next—a crazy upside down world of noise, foul smell, and fear. A trip to the fairground gone wrong, it was like a child's nightmare of being taken by his elder brother on a horrible big dipper which went mad. But grown ups don't shout out—hang on and watch the depth gauge . . . now reading 1000 feet.

Back and forward. Nightmares about the hook. Convinced the toggle was a hook which would suddenly loose its grip and send us back to the bottom. Why hadn't it come off when we were near the bottom. Not so far to fall. But now the depth read 900 feet. Too far to fall back without bursting our craft.

A sound of water inside our sphere. A leak. Oh Christ, not now. But it was the once carefully secured plastic bag containing guess what, and the urine bottle, also once full; both of them had burst. It is surprising how much two men can excrete over three and a half days, even without much to drink.

The lift had started at roughly 10.55 am. At 11.37 the depth was 650 feet—forty minutes so far and still the toggles held. Once more I tried in vain to talk to the surface, but the motion was even more violent as the length of line shortened.

A new sound burst on us. Air noise, and it was inside our sphere. That was bad, we could not afford to increase the pressure inside. Roger immediately knew what the trouble was; it was air leaking through the hull valves of the main air supply to the pilot's console. All this crashing about was beginning to take its effect. Luckily, without losing our hold, we could reach and turn off the supply valves. The hissing noise stopped.

At 11.42 the depth read 350 feet and then stopped. I had been watching the gauge like a hawk so noticed immediately it stopped. Communications were still non-existent but occasionally we heard a garbled message coming over, and we in turn passed our depth to the surface.

For over 15 minutes *PIII* stayed at 350 feet, crashing up and down. I tried contacting the surface every few seconds and then Roger took over.

Even though the rolling had been going on now for nearly an hour, we felt sure that at any minute the lines would part just as our tow line had broken before we were first dropped to the ocean bed. Snatches of instructions came over the loudspeaker:

'... lifting ... shortly. Trouble with ... confirm that ... unpinned. Over'

We became a little desperate.

'Surface for God's sake keep lifting ... crashing about. Hatch is unpinned. Please lift.'

What had happened was that the *CURV* tow line and lifting line had become entangled.

At last the lines were free and we started to move upwards again. 300 feet ... 200 feet ... Daylight. Actual daylight streaming in; we could catch glimpses of the lines streaming up towards the surface every time the submersible was itself looking up. Up and down, the pendulum much shorter now, the motion quicker and more violent.

In five minutes the depth gauge read 60 feet. From 1571 feet up to 60 feet in 80 minutes. How much longer? I was scared stiff but the daylight gave us hope.

The next time I looked at the gauge it was reading 100 feet. Were we sinking again? No, up we went, surging 40 feet while hanging beneath the ship, just as we had done before plunging to the ocean bottom.

This final horror was played out between 60 and 100 feet. It lasted for another 75 minutes—five and seventy minutes each one of which seemed to last a lifetime. The brutal motion continued and even got worse; All Roger and I could do to help was to keep clinging on, jamming ourselves as firmly as we could in opposite corners. Higher and higher went the mad dipper but still the lines held. No longer did I long to go back

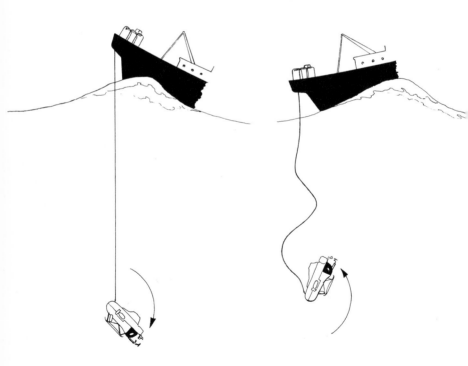

| SSEL | | SUBMERSIBLE | TASK  PIII RESCUE | CHARTER | | |
|---|---|---|---|---|---|---|
| BER | LOCATION | LAT. LONG | | | | |
| | DECCA | CHAIN | SEA STATE | WIND | | DATE |
| OFFICER | | | | | | |
| | HANDLING | | GEMINI | | DIVER(S) | |
| | CAPSTAN | | TRACKING | | | |

| Message |
|---|
| PIII HAS SEEN DIVER. |
| WHEN LG LIFT LINE IS ON BLOW ALL BALLAST. — NO REPLY. |
| PIII CALLS IN. 3 CANNOT GET BACK. |
| 9 REQUEST CAN CREW CLIMB OUT.? . PIII TALKS BACK — DISTORTED. |
| YES CAN CLIMBE OUT. |
| PIII HAS AIR LEAK WHEN VENTING. — LEAK IN SPHERE. |
| TOLD TO ISOLATE & CLOSE VALUE— |
| SURFACE SEQUENCE. |
| WILL BE ASKED TO BLOW MAIN HATCH & GET OUT WHEN CLEAR |
| OF WATER. |
| III REQUESTS SOMEONE TO BANG ON HATCH ON SURFACE. |
| III ASKS FOR ATMOSPHERIC PRESSURE. SURFACE GIVES 30.25 INS. |
| III ASKS FOR S.TREP. |
| S INFORMS III WE WILL UNDOG & OPEN THE HATCH. PIII AOK. |
| 45 FT. |
| PISCES III ON SURFACE |

to the seabed, instead I was in a frenzy just to get out and away from this horrific situation. I was sick but very little came up.

Next came the turn of the divers, who had the well nigh impossible task of attaching to *PIII* heavy enough lift lines for her to be hauled clear of the sea, as once out of the water she would weigh ten times as much. Several divers came down but failed to get anywhere near the submersible; we could hear them breathing over the loudspeaker and actually caught a glimpse of one.

Then Bob Hanley, the Field Officer who had been relieved by Ralph for our charter and was now back and diving, managed to 'ride' *PIII*, which he likened to a bucking bronco. Somehow a 15-ton shackle was attached to the lift point, and then Bob passed a nylon rope through it. He swam clear, then all the lines were middled up onboard *John Cabot*.

At last came the final lift. Just after 1 pm on Saturday 1st September 1973 *PIII* broke clear of the water. Even then no chances were taken. More lift lines were secured and a 40 cubic foot mine bag was attached to the lower shackle of the aft sphere—just in case.

Pisces III *breaks surface with two divers standing on her, and other divers standing by in* Geminis. *Below the divers wait to open the hatch and release the pilots.*

Roger and I had listened to all the bangs and crashes going on above us. We had previously been instructed to unpin our hatch from the inside so it could be opened by the divers when they were ready; we could well have been injured or knocked unconscious during the lift and would then have been unable to help ourselves. Somehow during the last hour I had managed to ask the surface for the atmospheric pressure; we had been told that it was 30.25 inches, and had adjusted the pressure inside to balance this using air and oxygen.

I remember looking at the oxygen gauge just before the hatch was opened. I read 200 psi; so two hours of the treatment we had suffered during the lift accounted for 600 psi fall in oxygen; at that rate some 20 minutes more dangling around with the lines entangled would have left our ration of oxygen in the cylinder at about zero.

However they'd done it, and as we cleared the water Roger and I found ourselves looking at each other again. The bucking motion had ceased and the submersible tilted forward looking down towards the surface of the sea.

*One of the divers crouches down to open the hatch.*

'You out first,' I said grinning. 'No, I'm the pilot and go second'. Roger could not swim so we agreed after all that he should leave the sphere first. There was a loud bang, the hatch was open and there was sunlight streaming in from above. Real voices spoke and hands reached down.

Roger shot up through the hatch and he had gone by the time I crawled out. Mike Bond, one of our divers, was there grinning from ear to ear as he clasped me round the shoulder in his diving suit. A Gemini came up and I stumbled down into it. We were alive and out in the fresh air. It was real.

*Released at last. Roger Mallinson is in the Gemini while Roger Chapman stands on the sail with one hand on the lifting rope while two divers support him.*

# 14. Home Again

So much happened in the next few days, but a few really important events stand out in my memory.

The trip across to *Voyager* in the Gemini just after rescue, and passing a strange looking object floating in the water. 'That's *CURV*' said Roy Browne, who was driving my Gemini. 'Oh'.

There were lines everywhere in the water and then a large RAF Nimrod aircraft flew very low close by. This made me look

*The author sits in the middle on the trip back to* Voyager *after rescue. Roy Browne, driving the Gemini, points out* CURV *to him.*

up, as I had been more interested in splashing salt water over my face and taking in great gulps of fresh air.

There were ships everywhere and more planes overhead. It was only then that I realised that it was a large red ship which we had just left, with *PIII* hanging precariously over its bow.

'Who's that Roy?'

'*John Cabot*'

I could not take it all in.

And then we were getting nearer the *Voyager* and Roy made the approach to the lifting point where the Gemini is hoisted.

'I'd rather climb up at the stern please Roy' I said. This is the place the divers normally get back onboard after a launch. I did not want to be lifted up by anything just for a little while.

'Sure you can manage OK?'

Back on deck then and feeling a little groggy and unsteady, but otherwise OK. There were a few people about, some I didn't recognise. And then I noticed the two submersibles *PV* and *PII* sitting on the hangar deck, and all around them were mounds and mounds of rope, shackles and wire, while the whole hangar deck and launch area was a mass of equipment, and more faces. This had truly been a mammoth operation and it was only just dawning on me. It was some days later that I fully realised how big an operation it had been.

I went into my cabin and saw on the desk my pilot's log open at the page for the next dive to be recorded. Before this dive my total piloting time had been 70½ hours. I tried to work out just how long we had been down and came up with the figure of 84½ hours, so that dive was longer than all my previous

*The entry in Roger Chapman's log is brief indeed.*

| ATE | DETAILS OF DIVING OPERATIONS | | DEPTH IN FEET | DURA-TION IN MINS. | EQUIP-MENT USED |
|---|---|---|---|---|---|
| 1/8. | *Pisces III* Dive Crew Brown. Pilot Lest Mathison oth Lost Commdr. | ? } | | | |
| | Longest Dive Deepest Rescue. | | 1675 | 84½ HR | PIII |

151

experience as a submersible pilot. I made a note in the log and there was a knock at the door. I went off to see the doctor and was given a cup of tea. It was good to be back.

There were many personal incidents that happened onboard *Voyager* before we were whisked away by helicopter to Cork and an incredible press reception at the airport. David Mayo burst into my cabin, having arrived back from *Hecate* where he had worked throughout the whole rescue.

'God, I'm glad to see you, shaking my hand strongly'. He was terribly white and looked worn out. David was the last to see us disappear beneath the waves and could easily have been caught up in *PIII* as she disappeared.

Everyone looked worn out. Cans of beer were everywhere but Roger and I, later, surrounded by friends, once again jammed in a small place, this time a cabin with fresh air blowing

*Surrounded by friends in* Voyager *celebrating with beer, the two rescued pilots stuck to lemonade.*

through an open porthole, drank lemonade. June telephoned and said 'You sound fine and very matter of fact', then she laughed. She had been marvellous back in Barrow, and had such faith in Vickers and the rescuers, that the news of our eventual recovery reached her in a pub along with George Henson, her boss.

However June should continue her own story since we left her at the end of chapter 10 with a heavy heart on Friday night.

'It must have been around 5 am when the phone rang and the marvellous news was given about the first rope being attached to *PIII*. Could it really be true that our luck had begun to change. I went back to bed and knowing one little bit of good news, slept until morning.

'Saturday morning was sunny and warm despite a high wind. I can remember the drive into Barrow so clearly. Two of our friends were getting married that day (Roger and I were supposed to be there) and it was my parents' 30th wedding anniversary. I sent two telegrams from Dalton Post Office, and with a great deal of courage signed them "June and Roger".

'At Base faces were cheering up noticeably. Most of the news filtering back was encouraging—another line had been attached, *CURV* was going down with a heavy lift line—oh yes, the rescuers were on the road to success, I felt convinced.

'The exact time of the various reports evades me but as far as I remember it must have been some time after 11 a.m. that the heavy lift line was attached and lift off was due to commence. Then reports came through that lift-off was successful and the crippled submersible was on its long journey to the surface. It was explained to me that *PIII* would be held at about 60 feet from the surface for a short period during which time other lines, brought down by divers, would be attached. No chances were going to be taken now.

It must have been around noon that we heard they were at that point some 60 feet down, so I phoned my mother—I just had to tell her the news as my parents were not on the rota for regular calls. As far as I was concerned Roger was home and dry—the possible snags had just not occurred to me.

'At this point, knowing there would be a delay before surfacing, I was taken to a pub for lunch. While we were sitting eating sandwiches a call came through for me, breaking the marvellous news that the boys were actually out of *PIII*, fit and well; far better than anyone had ever dared hope. The relief was terrific, indescribably great. All I wanted then was to see Roger.

Back in *Voyager*, Len Edwards, the Captain, had been standing so long on his bridge that his feet were terribly swollen. I found him in his cabin, feet up in the air and another huge grin. 'You buggers' he said 'I knew where you were all the time, but had terrible trouble convincing anyone else. All their fancy electronic gear'. And he did know. Seamanship, a sense of humour and straightforward talk. He was Captain of the ship.

Willie the cook came up and offered huge plate loads of food.

'Get it down y'ere'. But we weren't hungry and I didn't eat much for another 24 hours.

Peter Messervy arrived back from the *John Cabot* while I was drinking tea with Ralph Henderson. He stood there wearing a life jacket, smiling, but did not say much. He was Captain of the Company and had organised the rescue. He did not like too much fuss and was glad for us that the outcome had been successful.

Bob Eastaugh was still messing about in a Gemini organising the safe return of *PIII*. 'Tell Ralph I want some divers now,' he yelled over his wet portable radio. The rescue was over but he still had a submersible hanging over the end of someone else's ship. What a mess in there and the smell! I was right, he was horrified at the shambles but perhaps he had a twinkle in his eye.

And so it went on. Handshakes, cans of lemonade, cups of tea and a cigarette. An elderly doctor from Cork came in and held out his hand. I shook it but he wanted to take my pulse. He went away muttering . . . 'Incredible, nothing wrong with them'. And there wasn't.

Peter organised a helicopter and finally persuaded Bob Eastaugh to return with us to Cork. Roger and I, Peter, Bob and Al Trice, operations manager of HYCO, and one or two more were picked up and flown away. It was sad to go, when there were still some of the men we had no time to greet again. I hope they read this book, because we owe them so much.

From Cork, with the milling mass of photographers and news-men, a Vickers light aircraft flew us across the Irish Sea to

Barrow. The light was fading as the plane approached the small airfield and I was slightly dreading another hectic reception. But the gates to the grass airfield had been closed and there was just a small group of people standing in the wind.

I couldn't see much as I walked over to the group but noticed my wife June standing slightly apart wrapped up in a sheepskin coat against the weather.

'Hello honey', I said, now close to her.

'Hello Rog. It's so lovely to see you'.

# 15. Aftermath

There are still one or two things unanswered. How and why did the accident happen? Could a rope, in a rough sea, wrap itself round a small hexagonal locking nut, and turn it sufficiently to open the hatch? The hatch is now buried deep beneath the Atlantic, sunk into the soft mud not far from a telephone cable. If it were ever found, another reason may be given.

The enquiry report, with all the facts before them, concluded it was a chance in a million. Surely it must have been and major modifications have been carried out to the hatch to prevent it ever happening again.

Over the months I have been questioned, alone, and with Roger, 'What was it really like down there?' Was it cold and did you think you were going to die? It is not until you have time to think, and talk to other people, that a few of these questions can be answered.

There were certain times which I remember clearly when I was very scared that something fatal was about to happen. On the way down stern first to the seabed, watching the depth gauge, and having time to think and wonder whether the submersible could withstand the impact. Would our own hatch fly away? Totally illogical thinking as the pressure outside would have been far too great. But I was scared all the same. And then seconds after the impact, waiting in pitch darkness for the flood that never came. Moving about carefully, shaking violently right inside oneself and pretending to one's companion that you were cool as a cucumber.

The very first drip of condensation that fell on your face, again in the dark, and the immediate response of your body to find out if it was salt water and the leak was now starting. The torch went on, and time and again I would check each drip.

During the days that followed the cramps in my legs came and went. It was the dampness probably and disturbed my companion every time I moved. And we burnt up just that little more oxygen in those few seconds. I watched the tiny oxygen gauge slowly dropping towards empty. It was just the gauge that was telling us that time was running out. We could not taste the oxygen, and we hardly noticed its effect, yet we had to breathe and the oxygen was part of life. The headaches were something else. Pain we could understand, but a tiny gauge creeping towards zero was our clock. It did not even tick, just a constant reminder.

As the humidity reached its highest level our clothes became completely saturated. It was not all that cold inside our sphere, although the thermometer had been damaged on impact and we had no figure of temperature; but the dampness made it feel so cold. That is why we used each other for warmth.

And some have asked, with slightly raised eyebrows, how it was that during Roger's periods of extreme pain, a squeeze of the shoulder or hand meant so much. Two fully grown men behaving in this way?

But it was a way of communicating. The darkness, and the fact that we knew we must not talk. Yet I well knew that someone next to me was suffering—and it worked. We shared all we had, food, the one can of lemonade, oxygen, and there was little or no friction between us. We also shared an experience that has taught us a great deal. Tolerance, patience, and above all, the knowledge that people will work night and day to help others in trouble; they would not rest for one moment until all hope was past or success had been achieved. Thank you to all those people.

Finally comes a question I am often asked. 'Did this accident in *Pisces III* put you against diving again?' The answer is 'Not at all'. One can go through a terrible time lying ill in bed without being put off from going to bed. Both Roger Mallinson and I continued to dive in submersibles afterwards, sometimes together again. After a further twenty-five dives following the rescue, I tried an entirely different type of job which in time would have allowed me a more settled home life and indeed allowed me to get on with writing this book. Yet my longing to work at sea, and under the sea, proved too strong; as I write this aftermath I have already gone back to a diving job with submersibles again.

*Back to underwater work again, Roger Chapman is here seen inside the sphere of a sister submersible of* Pisces III.

# 16. Broughton's Tale

By Bryan Tyson

'Roger works for that Company.' There was a small piece in the *Guardian* about an incident in the Atlantic involving a submarine of some sort. It wasn't in my wife's *Times*, therefore she considered it hadn't happened yet and maybe never would. It was the word 'Oceanics' that had caught my eye. Roger had mentioned it and that he sometimes had access to Scotch lobsters which he caught in a Walter Mitty sort of way from a miniature submarine. Some months before, Roger Chapman bought the house next door in New Street, Broughton in Furness, at that time in Lancashire.

Broughton is a small town—not a village as many accidental visitors suppose. As they are usually going somewhere else it takes them by surprise. They drive in and its gone before they know it. Starting from Broughton almost everywhere is up with the exception of the Parish Church of St Mary Magdalen which for no plausible reason I've ever heard is tucked away in a hollow, out of town, out of sight from nearly any aspect you choose—but its presence felt, and distinctly. But even there you have to go up to go down. There is a disproportionately large square—a gift to the townspeople from a previous Lord of the Manor who miscalculated the future for wool in the district, underestimated a fishing village called Barrow in Furness and made a splendid and delightfully wrong assumption about the importance of Broughton. As a town it shows large on maps of the district because there is a shortage of other places—but it is small and offcomers are noticed.

Cornel Wilde was in the Square one day one summer recently, making a film with electricians from London streaming artificial sun through the windows of the Manor Arms while sweating themselves in the natural sun. More or less the whole town passed through the Square that day. Casually, of course with no show of being in any way impressed. Branwell Bronte spent six sober months at Broughton House in the town some years ago—as a tutor I believe. The present Duke of Edinburgh had a lunch of lamb and a glass of local bitter at the Old King's Head. A tanker spilled diesel all over the main street one time. And there have been other events, but nothing to prepare Broughton for what happened.

So, Roger Chapman bought the house next door. I was ready to dislike him for that alone. Or if he altered the panelled doors in his house which are identical to the ones in mine because both houses years ago were one. We overlook a closed and cobbled courtyard with roses and ivy and weeds. It's shared with the Brocklebanks, Mister and Missus, quite old and very gentle church people whose bright blue home with two other cottages make up one side of the yard, and Harry Douglas who was a cobbler in the days when my father delivered milk to houses here, and who now grows prize winning tomatoes and offers detailed advice on how to rid the yard of weeds. 'All together. That's how it's done. Pick a nice day. Then everybody who lives round the yard sets to work on a patch. We all have tea out there—and that's how it gets done.' Roger and I had been discussing bringing back this practical bit of sociable living but, he explained, he was off on a tour of duty that week. We'd get down to it when he returned next month.

We were surprised rather then shocked when we realised that Roger was one of the men inside *Pisces III*. First press reports were understandably thin on facts but it did come across pretty clearly that there was no real cause for concern. There had been a mishap. The submarine was on the bed of the sea. But they knew where it was. Constant contact. They were talking to the men, who were uninjured and had plenty of air to breathe. Vickers, stuffed to the gunwhales with professional expertise were right on top of the job. Simple. I made up my mind that Friday night in the King's was going to be greatly enriched by the pulling of Roger's leg. Absent without leave? Tut tut.

A colleague who had been in the Navy during the war commented that 'Nothing is simple at sea.' and if his usual reminiscences hadn't been quite so Monsarrat I might have taken more note. As it was it was perfectly obvious that Roger was in no danger. What had happened to him was interesting—but no more so than if he'd won the pools or been arrested. The marvel of the minute. Soon over and done with, easily forgotten. But it did not go away. A few hours routine work did not solve the problem.

Roger was headlines. The serious faces on television were talking about him. Everything about him became important and the world wanted to know. It couldn't have happened to a more inappropriate person. Roger cherishes his privacy, respects his colleagues, loves his wife and family, enjoys the company of friends and that's enough. He's at ease in company but possibly even more so spending hours making good a piece of furniture he's brought home from the sale room, or doing nothing in particular with a fine display of industry. This man of very private satisfactions was now a celebrity, a brave voyager, very likely a hero.

'Roger isn't going to like all this fuss.' It was a shrewd summing up from one of the neighbours. It also made us laugh. There couldn't possibly be any chance of Roger coming to any harm because he'd have to come back to dismiss all the fuss with a hard stare and a cool disclaimer.

The radio was reassuring at this time. The town looked normal. June phoned Jinny Steele. Now Jinny can be as kind as a mother and hard as any father when need be. June needed all the fathers and mothers she could muster at that time. She asked Jinny to see that the house was alright and the cats were fed and looked after. She wanted that problem off her mind. She wouldn't be coming home herself for a while. It was not so much what they said on the radio and television. The news was still encouraging. True there were minor snags. Time slip. Back up resources were being marshalled from all over the world. But when you've heard and read about other disasters you hear things in the spaces between words. It was not quite as straightforward as it had seemed. And you tell yourself to be sensible. You try to crush the thoughts taking shape in your head and you certainly don't speak of them.

Outside his own skill a man is frequently a fool, either inventing problems or dismissing them with one sweep of a statement.

'Good God, they know where it is. Tie a bloody rope on it and get pulling.'

But slowly, against our will, we were having to face a fact however ridiculous. They didn't know where Pisces was. Once they'd got men to the hard news centres at Barrow, out in the Atlantic, at Cork and around the world the Press wanted the background. They came into Broughton, first by phone then by taxi, their questions veneered with concern for Mr Chapman and of course Mrs Chapman. They were everywhere.

They didn't like us. They didn't like Broughton. It was a perversity they had never got used to the fact that important things sometimes choose unimportant places to happen. They wanted to know where June was. Was she pretty? Did we have a photograph? Any photograph. They wanted Jinny to say the cats were pining. They wanted to buy anybody a pint. A whisky, a large one, a bottle—for something the other papers hadn't got. They all wanted phones at the same time and 'Are you quite sure you don't know where Mrs Chapman is?'

You couldn't blame them for not liking us. There was nothing we could say that could help Roger and June—therefore nothing we could say mattered. They didn't agree and kept on trying. To have been a parent at Aberfan must have been a very particular sort of hell.

A reporter and a photographer talked and pushed their way into Roger's house. 'How much did they pay for this place? How much does he earn? Did he ever talk about the danger of his work. Did he ever talk about death.

The radio was never off. There seemed to be no gaps between the newsflashes. If anything else was happening in the world nobody mentioned it. We were saturated with information and knew nothing. A Vickers man came into the King's and held court at the bar on the strength of his special connection. He was from the wages office, nevertheless we listened attentively to him—for there might just have been something he'd heard.

There was a whisper that June was coming home to pick up a change of clothes. She was at Urswick, staying with friends in

Wales; with Sir Leonard Renshaw in London; at Barrow; flying to Cork, or perhaps even going to talk to Roger on the telephone. The reporters wanted to know when she was coming. But they didn't know for sure she'd been until she'd gone. A few people glanced at her through the car window. They said she looked pale and added 'Poor girl'.

Then everything was going to be alright after all. A special newsflash interrupted the programme, except by this time it felt that the news was occasionally interrupted by music. They'd got a line onto *Pisces*. They were lifting. Roger was as good as home.

But it wasn't true.

Roger is in a bad way. He's rambling. $CO_2$ poisoning. Time was running out. Everybody had a view on how long the air would last—and nobody, not even the experts, knew. The weather was getting worse.

'They're singing now. They must be delirious.'

And that wasn't true either.

We didn't know what to believe. The Vicar was asked if prayer would help. He believed it would.

Fifteen hundred and seventy five feet—that's how far down he was. Pace out that distance across the town and you've covered it from end to end. No distance at all.

Stephen Fry wasn't reckoned by a lot of people to know much about anything. Stephen saw things in very simple terms and now he didn't like what he saw. He stood at our door with tears in his eyes—and we couldn't honestly say he was wrong.

Then we heard about *CURV*. Everybody knows what America can do. Maybe faith can move mountains but its prudent to have a big bulldozer on standby. They can moonwalk, surely they could catch a little submarine.

The news sounded good but there was a determination not to believe.

'There's many a slip.'

'They must be about jiggered.'

The papers were saying that fatigue was becoming a problem among the rescuers.

'If they can't bloody well start a simple bloody outboard what chance with this *CURV* thing?'

The experts in whose skill we had placed our confidence

at the start were now 'feckless buggers' who had not only lost the sub in the first place, then couldn't remember where they'd put it, then cheated us with their cocky 'no problem'. We were not prepared to forgive them or trust them and we did not want to be fair.

We woke up tired on Saturday. First optimism, then a surge of fear. Alternate that over a few days and people do get tired. Like a wet childhood Sunday that Saturday morning went on for ever.

There are people in and around Broughton who haven't even passed the time of day with certain other people for a generation and more. That morning nobody was ignored by anybody. It was truce.

'Are they going to get him up do you think?'

'Maybe. But what must it have done to his mind?'

So another fear was added. And the lifting of *Pisces* went on. Three foot up, two foot back it seemed.

Then all at once people came out of their houses smiling. Cars stopped and those people got out. Everybody talking to whoever was nearest.

'They're up.'

'Safe.'

'Both well.'

'It's right. It's on the news. They're flying to Cork. June's gone out there.'

It was England winning the World Cup, it was Land of my Fathers to a Welshman away from home, it was becoming a father for the first time all over again. It was painfully personal and at the same time shared generously. People had heard it on the news, now they wanted to hear other people—people they knew—say it. They wanted to have it repeated to make it even more true. Miss Butler was in her beautiful garden. . . .

'Have you heard? I'm so grateful' she said.

Mr Brocklebank was there, hopping with excitement in the middle of the courtyard.

'They're up. They're up. Oh Mr Tyson, we did pray for them.' He shook my hand and we hugged each other. I shook Mrs Brocklebank's hand.

'Do you know I couldn't eat my breakfast this morning.' he said.

'I'm going to have such a good tea.'

'You'd have thought we'd pulled off the rescue between us. Oh the experts were back in favour now—at least they were with most folk.

'What an achievement!' 'What an effort!' 'Deepest ever submarine rescue.' 'Should never have happened in the first place.'

'Well it should get a line or two in the Guinness Book of Records. I've a good mind to write and tell them.'

'Nay. They're bound to have noticed it in the papers.' There were no banners across the street when Roger did come home—just handshakes, and that suited him fine.

He was deeper inside himself, perhaps he'd learnt something most other men haven't. He was speaking even more softly than usual, his eyes on other things, not really with us. And June—she'd taken back responsibility for herself again. Neat, efficient. She was moving things around her kitchen, touching things for the sheer love of it, making it real again. A car drew up outside the house. They didn't wind the windows down although it was a very hot day. They just gawped at Roger's house and in less than a minute they were off in the direction of Coniston Water. That's where Donald Campbell killed himself. The incident isn't often spoken of now—and that also suits Roger.

# Appendix—Timetable of Event

*Wednesday 29th August 1973*

0115  Dive commenced
0345  *PIII* working at 1650 feet
0800  Completed dive, ready to return to the surface.
0918  On the surface being recovered.
0922  Towline fouls aft sphere hatch, hatch off, sphere flooded.
0925  On the way to the bottom stern first.
0930  On bottom.
0945  Both pilots OK. Depth 1575 feet.
1000  Vickers at Barrow informed by radio telephone that life support indications were that the oxygen supplies would last until early Saturday morning.
1035  Support ship *Vickers Venturer* contacted in the North Sea and ordered to return *PII* to nearest port.
1046  The President of International Hydrodynamics Ltd (HYCO) in Canada contacted and the assistance of *PII* requested.
1209  The Royal Navy ordered *HMS Hecate* to the accident area with special ropes.
1455  RAF Nimrod aircraft flies over *Vickers Voyager* standing by *PIII* until relieved by another ship.
1507  United States Salvage Dept offered *CURV* (Controlled Under Water Recovery Vehicle) then in California.
1630  United States Navy offered *John Cabot* then in Swansea, South Wales. Offer accepted.
2020  Commander Messervy, General Manager of Vickers Oceanics, and base support team left in Vickers aircraft bound for Cork.

*Thursday, 30th August 1973*

0330   *PV* in Royal Canadian Air Force Hercules aircraft arrived at Cork, Southern Ireland, from North Sea.

0412   *PII* arrived by RAF Hercules aircraft at Cork from Canada.

0815   *Vickers Voyager* arrived Cork after relief on station by other ships.

0835   *John Cabot* arrives at Cork

1030   Loading of *PII* and *PV* complete and *Vickers Voyager* sailed from Cork.

1940   *CURV* arrived at Cork and transferred to *John Cabot*.

*Friday, 31st August 1973*

0100   *Vickers Voyager* arrived on station with *PII* and *PV*.

0200   *PII* launched with 8-inch polypropylene rope attached to special toggle.

0240   *PII* nearing the seabed. Line is torn from manipulator due to buoyancy of rope.

0430   *PII* recovered onboard *Voyager*, repairs to manipulator started.

0545   *PV* launched equipped with 4-inch polypropylene line attached to special snap hook.

0615   *PV* on the seabed looking for *PIII*.

0940   *PV* unable to find *PIII*. Ordered to the surface to be towed back into the correct position.

1100   *PV* on the way down again.

1244   *PIII* is found by *PV* and attempt is made to attach the snap hook. Attempt failed.

      (*PV* stays next to *PIII* making further unsuccessful attempts until she is finally recovered at 0040 Saturday.)

1730   *John Cabot* and *CURV* arrive at accident area.

1950   *PII* launched. Immediate recovery ordered after emergency indication of water in her own aft sphere.

2015   *PII* recovered. Repair started.

2359   *CURV* has electrical fault and cannot be launched for at least 4 hours.

SATURDAY 1st September 1973

0043  PV recovered very low on power.
0402  PII launched with toggle and 3½-inch polypropylene line.
0437  PII on bottom close to PIII.
0505  First toggle, with 3½-inch line placed in PIII's aft sphere.
0600  An attempt is made by PII to attach choker of PV's line to lift point. Attempt fails.
0800  PII recovered by Voyager.
0940  CURV is launched from the John Cabot with another toggle and a 6-inch braided nylon line.
1030  CURV homing in.
1035  CURV has positive lock with toggle inserted in aft sphere opening.
1050  Lifting of PIII starts.
1109  PIII reports leaving the seabed—rocking about.
1142  PIII at 350 feet; lifting stopped whilst CURV is disentangled.
1205  PIII at 100 feet. Divers working to attach heavy lift lines.
1247  All ropes heaved together.
1317  PIII lifted clear of the water and hatch opened. Both pilots disembarked into Geminis and thence to Voyager.